God's Invitation

A Challenge to College Students

Richard Blackaby &
Henry Blackaby

LifeWay Press
Nashville, Tennessee

7200-38
ISBN 0-8054-9679-3
Dewey Decimal Classification: 248.834
Subject Heading: Christian Life/College

Unless otherwise noted, Scripture quotations are from the Holy Bible,
New International Version,
copyright © 1973, 1978, 1984 by International Bible Society

Printed in the United States of America

Art Herron
Editor
Connie Taillon
Assistant Editor
Bill Henry
Director, National Student Ministry

Edward Crawford
Art Director
Liz Gibson
Graphic Designer
Lynn Wells
Manager, Art Design Section

**Free teacher helps are available through Compuserve on
SBC Net in the Student Ministry folder.**

You can also obtain them by:
Telephone: 615•251•2777
Fax: 615•251•3953
Mail: 127 Ninth Avenue, North, Nashville, TN 37234-0153

LifeWay Press
127 Ninth Avenue, North
Nashville, Tennessee 37234

CONTENTS

THE AUTHORS

Henry Blackaby

Richard Blackaby

Henry Blackaby has enjoyed working with college students and is a popular speaker at student meetings. Henry grew up in Canada and earned a B.A. from the University of British Columbia. He earned his B.Div. and Th.M. from Golden Gate Baptist Theological Seminary and a D.D. from Hardin Simmons University. As a pastor in Canada, Henry sensed that in order to reach the nation for Christ, God would have to call college students to Himself and then send them out as pastors, missionaries and church workers across the land. With this in mind, he founded a Bible college where students could study the Scriptures and hear God's call upon their lives. During Henry's time as a pastor, numerous college students were baptized and many of these felt called into full-time Christian service.

He now serves as a special consultant to the presidents of the Home and Foreign Mission Boards as well as the Sunday School Board of the Southern Baptist Convention in the area of Prayer and Spiritual Awakening.

Henry is a popular conference speaker and has written several books including: *Experiencing God: Knowing and Doing the Will of God, Fresh Encounter: God's Pattern for Revival and Spiritual Awakening, Called and Accountable, What the Spirit is Saying to the Churches, Lift High the Torch,* and *When God Speaks: How to Recognize God's Voice and Respond in Obedience.* He was the general editor for the *Experiencing God Study Bible.* Henry has been a keen observer of revival and spiritual awakening. He participated in the recent moving of God on the campus of Howard Payne University in Brownwood, Texas.

Henry and his wife Marilynn have five children, all of whom have responded to God's call into full-time Christian ministry.

Richard Blackaby is the oldest child of Henry and Marilynn and has worked extensively with college students. He graduated from the University of Saskatchewan where he served as the president of the Baptist Student Union. During that time, Richard met his wife Lisa Cavanaugh, who was also on the student council. Richard was the vice-president and then president of the state student council of the Northwest Baptist Convention. He earned an M.Div. and Ph.D. from Southwestern Baptist Theological Seminary. Richard and Lisa have three children: Michael, Daniel and Carrie.

Richard was the pastor of Friendship Baptist Church in Winnipeg, Manitoba, before becoming president of the Canadian Southern Baptist Seminary in Cochrane, Alberta, Canada. He previously co-authored *When God Speaks: How to Recognize God's Voice and Respond in Obedience* with his father. He is a frequent speaker at student conferences and has counseled with many students considering God's call upon their lives to full-time Christian service.

INTRODUCTION

As a college student you are at a most important and vulnerable time in your life. A serious Christian will want to prepare and become equipped for God's best. Life is so precious. How you use the life God has given you is critical. Strive to invest your life in such a way that you will have no regrets and will know that your life has been well spent.

You may be in an environment where others influence and pressure you to conform to their values, goals, and lifestyles. This can lead you to "lose it all." But remember, as a Christian, you will always have the presence of the Holy Spirit in your life, exerting a significant influence to go His way which always leads to abundant life. Jesus warned people to *"Enter through the narrow gate. For wide is the gate and broad is the road that leads to destruction, and many enter through it. But small is the gate and narrow the road that leads to life, and only a few find it"* (Matthew 7:13-14).

I am confident that college students truly want life, not destruction. This course of study is designed to help you experience God; that is to know in your life His ways, His promises, His presence, and His abundant life. Read the Scriptures carefully for *"they are your very life"* (John 6:63; Deuteronomy 30:11-20). Study with others who are also wanting to experience God. Choose to be accountable to one or more persons who will confront you when they see you making wrong choices which lead you away from God's best. Spend time early, and throughout the day to *"seek the Lord with all your heart"* in prayer (Deuteronomy 4:29). *Remember*, God already has wonderful plans for you, "to give you a hope and a future . . ." (Jeremiah 29:11-13). God will guide you daily as you study this course and earnestly seek His will.

It is my pleasure to write once again with my oldest son Richard. Together we have sought to clearly describe how you can experience the joy of knowing and walking with God. I have appreciated my wife Marilynn and Richard's wife Lisa as they have been so supportive of our ministries to college students over the years. I am delighted to work with Connie Taillon as an assistant editor for this project. I baptized Connie as well as her husband Gerry when they were college students. I never dreamed she would one day be editing a course I was writing for college students, nor that her husband would be the national director for evangelism and language missions for his convention in Canada. Thanks also go to Wayne Cook and Jerry Nash for their valuable contributions.

> "Enter through the narrow gate. For wide is the gate and broad is the road that leads to destruction, and many enter through it. But small is the gate and narrow the road that leads to life, and only a few find it."
>
> **Matthew 7:13-14**

100
50
0

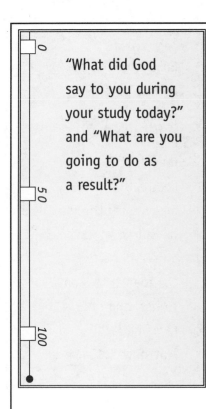

"What did God say to you during your study today?" and "What are you going to do as a result?"

ABOUT THIS STUDY

The purpose of this course is to help you know what God is saying to you and to give practical help as you seek God's will for important decisions such as choosing your career and marriage partner. Our aim is to help college students be prepared for the life decisions they will face. This is a Bible study, so keep your Bible handy and look up each verse as directed. Our *advice* cannot change your life, but God's Word can.

There are seven chapters which can be covered in seven weeks: one chapter per week. There are five lessons in each chapter. Only one lesson should be completed each day to allow time to contemplate the truths you encounter. This study involves much more than the completion of assignments or the reading of a book: its purpose is for you to encounter God. That will not happen if you rush through the materials, neglect to read all the Scriptures, or cram the hour before your group meets!

There is a weekly Scripture memory verse that will help you remember the key truths of each chapter. If you are not experienced in Scripture memorization, the information below offers suggestions that others have found helpful.

1. Read the verse and think about its meaning.
2. Write the verse on index cards, one phrase per card.
3. Glance at the first phrase and say it aloud. Glance at the second phrase and say both phrases aloud. Continue this process until you have said the entire verse.
4. Try to say the verse later in the day. If you cannot remember the verse, look at the cards to refresh your memory.
5. Repeat the verse several times each day for a week or until you feel that it is firmly implanted in your mind.

At the end of each week you will meet with your group to discuss the materials you have studied and to share what God said to you. A group leader should be available to facilitate discussion. His role is not to lecture or impart new materials but to lead people to discuss what they have learned that week and what they have committed themselves to do in response.

At the end of each lesson you will be asked "What did God say to you during your study today?" and "What are you going to do as a result?" Use the allotted space as well as the wide margins in your book to keep a journal of what you are hearing God say. You may want to review all God said to you during the study. If your group feels that God is speaking to them and they need more time to process what He is saying, they may choose to use two weeks to cover each chapter in order to better understand and respond to Him.

0   10   20   40   100

INTRODUCTION

As George Bernard Shaw, the great English playwright, neared the end of his illustrious career, a young man approached him with an intriguing question. He asked, "If you could live your life over and could be any person you have ever known or could be any person in history, who would you want to be?" This was a provocative question, for Shaw had known some of history's greatest men and had been a friend of Winston Churchill. He replied, "I would be the man George Bernard Shaw COULD have been, but never was." How tragic to come to the end of your life and realize that you have never reached your full potential.

In contrast, my son Richard and I recently spent an inspiring evening in the home of an elderly Christian couple. The husband had been diagnosed with terminal, inoperable cancer; his life would end just one month later. As we sat with them in their living room, he reminisced with joy about how God had led him into politics for over 40 years of civil service. He talked about his Christian radio ministry and all the Christian leaders he had befriended. He and his wife rejoiced that their only son, a believer, had also entered politics and was now a prominent national figure. With great delight they told us that each of their five grandchildren loved God and were seeking to serve Him. Here was a godly man satisfied with his life and ready to die.

Some people face death grudgingly, resentfully, even fearfully. Others approach it with a sense of peace, satisfaction, and triumph. It is our hope that you will live your life in such a way that when the end is near, you will have the assurance of a life well spent. This will only happen if you link your life to God's eternal purposes.

LESSON 1
God Sees from an Eternal View

William Borden was born into a wealthy Chicago family in 1887. He had the best this world had to offer: education, world travels, and every physical comfort. By the age of 21 he was a millionaire. Yet Borden's heart was sensitive to God's will for his life. When he was seven he gave his life to Christ, but it was as a 16-year-old that God began to speak to him very specifically.

During an around-the-world cruise, he met missionaries going to their fields of service. Writing to his mother at the time he commented: "Your request that I pray to

MEMORY VERSE:

"For the Lord Almighty has purposed, and who can thwart him? His hand is stretched out, and who can turn it back?"
Isaiah 14:27

THIS WEEK'S LESSONS:

Lesson 1
God Sees
from an Eternal View

Lesson 2
God Extends
an Invitation

Lesson 3
God Follows a Pattern

Lesson 4
God Invites Us
to an Intimate
Relationship

Lesson 5
God Calls
to a Definite Choice

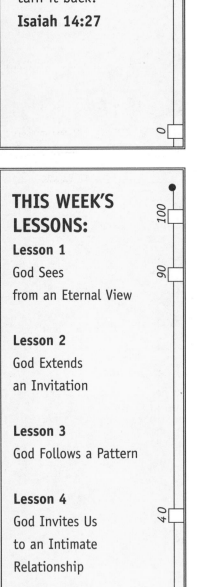

God for His very best plan for my life is not a hard thing to do, for I have been praying that very thing for a long time. . . . When I look ahead a few years it seems as though the only thing to do is to prepare for the foreign field."

Borden attended Princeton University with the intention of devoting his life to foreign missions. Despite the fact that he loved automobiles, he told his friends that he could not "afford" to purchase one. In reality, every time he considered buying a car, he was overwhelmed with the needs of foreign missions and sent money to those causes instead. It is estimated that during his three years in seminary he gave away over $70,000!

In December 1912, his education completed, Borden sailed to Cairo, Egypt for language training before entering mission service in China. While there, Borden contracted cerebral meningitis and died, never having reached his destination. Upon his deathbed, at age 25, he reiterated his life's theme: "No reserve, no retreat, no regrets." In his will he left almost $1,000,000 to Christian causes.

When news arrived in America that this young millionaire had willingly abandoned his fortune and died in squalid conditions in Egypt, it had an electrifying effect on college students across North America and Europe. Many students responded to God's call to missions because of Borden's life that had been tragically cut short.[1]

Questions:
• Do you consider Borden's life a success? Why or why not?

yes. even though he did not get to accomplish all he wanted to, he still helped + ministered in a great way

• Could *you* make the same sacrifices Borden did if you sensed God's leading? Why or why not?

with His help I believe I could because nothing is impossible as long as you believe

• What do you think motivated William Borden?

the desire to lead others to Christ so they would know Him as he did

God did not create you for time, but for eternity. Every word, act, and purpose of God is in the context of His *eternal* perspective. God never acts for the moment, but works with the full knowledge of all that has occurred throughout history leading up to the present time. He does not speak or act in your life without knowing what the consequences will be throughout the remainder of human history and eternity. From a human perspective, William Borden's life may have been tragically wasted. From God's *eternal* perspective, it was wisely spent.

God Knows Your Past
Notice God's eternal perspective on your life. Read Ephesians 1:4 and Jeremiah 1:5.

Questions:

• According to these verses, at what point did God begin preparing for your life?

<u>In the womb</u>

• What has happened in your past which would be important for God to know as He guides your life today?

<u>I have made mistakes that could have been avoided had I obeyed my mom</u>

When God relates to you He knows everything about you. He is aware of even the smallest details concerning your ancestors and every gene that they have passed down to you. He understands where your shyness came from as well as your intelligence. He knows the origin of every physical weakness and strength. He not only knows what you are like but He knows what has caused you to be who you are.

God Knows Your Future

God's eternal perspective is not limited to looking at the past. He also sees the future. *Read carefully what the Scripture to the right says about this.*

Questions:

• *Underline those things listed in the verses to the right that indicate what God knows about your future.*

• Check the concerns you have about your future in the following spaces:

☑ your future wife/husband   ☑ your future job/career
☑ having children   ☑ your future health
☑ length of your life   ☐ your success in business
☐ owning your own home   ☑ health of your parents
☑ crises you will face   ☐ world peace
☑ time of Christ's return   ☑ impact you will have on your world

• List ways God's knowledge of your future affects the way He leads you.

<u>He knows what He is doing and whether or not we know, He knows what is best for us so He can lead us down the right path</u>

God knows everything about your future. He foresees what crises you will face as well as every triumph you will enjoy. Because God sees your future, He is able to guide you perfectly day by day. He knows whether it is best for you to be married, to have children, or to remain single. Only God has perfect hindsight as well as foresight and so only He can guide you flawlessly. Just as Jesus confronted His followers, so He challenges you today. He knows what there is around you that has eternal significance and what will pass away before the year ends.

"I make known the end from the beginning, from ancient times, what is still to come. I say: My purpose will stand, and I will do all that I please . . . . What I have said, that I will bring about; what I have planned, that will I do."
Isaiah 46:10-11

"Your eyes saw my substance, being yet unformed. And in your book they all were written, the days fashioned for me, when as yet there were none of them."
Psalm 139:16

"Come, you who are blessed by my Father; take your inheritance, the kingdom prepared for you since the creation of the world."
Matthew 25:34

Question:
List two ways you are presently investing in eternity.
1. paying my tithes
2. reading my bible

God Speaks to You by the Holy Spirit
Have you ever said: "It would be easy to live the Christian life if I could just SEE Jesus and HEAR Him speaking to me?" Perhaps the Christian life might be easier in some ways but you would not be as compelled to live your life by faith, and as the writer of Hebrews pointed out: *"Without faith it is impossible to please God" (Hebrews 11:6).* Jesus promised His followers that He would not abandon them but the heavenly Father would send the Holy Spirit who would relate to the disciples in *exactly the same way* Jesus had.

> *Read the verses to the left and notice what the Holy Spirit does in your life.*

"He will give you another Counselor to be with you forever — the Spirit of truth." **John 14:16**

"When he comes, he will convict the world of guilt in regard to sin and righteousness and judgment. . . . But when he, the Spirit of truth, comes, he will guide you into all truth. . . . he will tell you what is yet to come." **John 16:7-8, 13**

"The Spirit searches all things, even the deep things of God. For who among men knows the thoughts of a man except the man's spirit within him? In the same way no one knows the thoughts of God except the Spirit of God." **1 Corinthians 2:10b-11**

Questions:
• Go back and underline the names given to the Holy Spirit which describe His activity in your life.

• What will the Holy Spirit do in your life?
He will guide you into all truths

It is the role of the Holy Spirit to lead and teach you in the same way that Jesus related to His disciples. Whether it is knowing what your major in college should be, or whom to marry, or what job to pursue, the Holy Spirit will guide you. It is imperative, therefore, that you cultivate your personal relationship with the Spirit of God so that you can clearly hear His voice.

• What did God say to you during your study today?
that He will lead me in the right direction as long as I listen.

• What will you do as a result?
I will pray every day and have a period when I just sit and listen to hear what He has to say.

LESSON 2
God Extends an Invitation
I am a keen observer of current events. I watch the national leaders on television and read about world affairs in the newspaper. Although I pray for my government leaders, I had never known them personally. Then one day I received an invitation to visit the President of the United States in the Oval Office. When I discussed issues of concern with the President, I knew I was speaking with someone who actually had the power to make a difference.

Had I lobbied and campaigned to gain the opportunity to speak to the President, I might never have been successful. Instead, I received an invitation, and by that invitation I was given immediate and personal access. This is similar to the Christian experience. We can go through life observing events taking place around us. We can discuss them with our family and friends and yet be oblivious to any way that we can make a difference. Suddenly God may reveal that He is present and active right in the midst of these events. The Bible calls this *revelation*. God shows us something that we could not have discovered on our own. The writer of Proverbs observed: *"Where there is no revelation, the people cast off restraint" (Proverbs 29:18)*. This means that without God's revelation, you will have no sense of direction nor will you lead a purposeful life guided toward God's best. Spiritual truth is revealed; it is not discovered. When God presents truth to you, His revelation is also His invitation to adjust your life to that truth.

God Extends an Invitation

When God told Noah that a flood was coming, it was something Noah never could have discovered on his own (until it was too late!). But once Noah understood the truth God had revealed, he immediately adjusted his life to God's word. God's revelation had also been an invitation for Noah to adjust his life to God's activity of judgment on the land. Noah did not *have* to accept God's invitation, but to *reject* it would have been disastrous. When God told Moses He was going to rescue the children of Israel out of Egypt, His revelation also came with an invitation. Moses had to make a choice. He could no longer herd sheep in the wilderness *and* remain obedient to the revelation he had received from God. From *Genesis* to *Revelation* God speaks to His people, calling, teaching, and guiding. While you are in college God will be seeking to guide you into His best.

God Speaks to You Through the Bible

As the Holy Spirit lives in you and guides you, He will use Scriptures to encourage, convict, and lead you to experience the full life that only God can give.

Read the verses to the right and notice how God uses the Bible to help you understand His will.

Question:

• List the things God says He will do for you as you obey His word.

you will be prosperous and successful, whatever you ask shall be given, you may be thoroughly equipped for every good work

Watch carefully as you read and study God's word. What the Spirit is teaching is God's will for your life (1 Corinthians 2:9-10). As you read the Bible each day, the Holy Spirit will guide you through verses which reveal God's will.

For example, you may be reading your Bible and come across *Matthew 15:4 "For God said, 'Honor your father and mother.'"* The Holy Spirit may focus your attention on this verse. You try to continue reading but you cannot leave verse four. You begin to have the uneasy feeling that God is applying this verse to you. You realize that your

"Do not let this Book of the Law depart from your mouth; meditate on it day and night, so that you may be careful to do everything written in it. Then you will be prosperous and successful." **Joshua 1:8**

"If you remain in me and my words remain in you, ask whatever you wish, and it will be given you." **John 15:7**

"All Scripture is God-breathed and is useful for teaching, rebuking, correcting and training in righteousness, so that the man of God may be thoroughly equipped for every good work." **2 Timothy 3:16-17**

"Call to me and I will answer you and tell you great and unsearchable things you do not know." **Jeremiah 33:3**

"So I say to you: Ask and it will be given to you; seek and you will find; knock and the door will be opened to you. For everyone who asks receives; he who knocks finds; and to him who knocks, the door will be opened." **Luke 11:9-10**

"In the same way, the Spirit helps us in our weakness. We do not know what we ought to pray for, but the Spirit himself intercedes for us with groans that words cannot express. And he who searches our hearts knows the mind of the Spirit, because the Spirit intercedes for the saints in accordance with God's will."
Romans 8:26-27

parents have done some things which have made you angry and you have held bitterness in your heart. You remember some of the painful words you exchanged the last time you were together. The Holy Spirit affirms that nothing they have done caused them to deserve the lack of respect you showed. You realize that God takes this extremely seriously and so you repent and take action to restore your relationship with your parents. God has just used the Bible to guide you.

Questions:
• What is one thing you have heard God saying to you recently as you read His word?

I'm not as worthless and lost as I feel and think I am

• How have you acted upon it?

I have tried to see myself as He sees me. I tell myself I have purpose and if I didn't I wouldn't be here.

God Speaks to You Through Prayer

The Holy Spirit will also speak to you during your times of prayer. Prayer is not a one-way conversation where you tell God all *your* plans and concerns. When you come into the presence of almighty God, what *He* says is far more important than what you want to say. God will speak to you in your prayer time if you will listen. *Notice in the Scripture to the left what God wants to tell you during your prayer times.*

Questions:
• Underline the things God promises to do when you pray.

• What does God show you when you pray?

God *does* have a will for your life. As you pray, God speaks His will to you. God spoke to Moses on Mount Sinai (Exodus 32:7-14), to Daniel in captivity (Daniel 9), and to Jesus during His earthly ministry (Matthew 17:1-8, 26:36-46). When you pray, alone or with others, be alert to any prompting of the Holy Spirit, for He will be speaking God's will to you.

For example, you may be praying one day when suddenly the Holy Spirit brings to mind a mission project to the homeless that your college group is planning to undertake. You did not sign up to help because you feel uncomfortable around homeless people. You try to return to what you were praying about but you cannot seem to forget the mission project. Then the Spirit brings to mind *Matthew 25:35: "For I was hungry and you gave me something to eat, I was thirsty and you gave me something to drink, I was a stranger and you invited me in."* The Spirit reminds you that Christ left the comforts of heaven to come and minister to mankind and that Jesus Himself had no place to lay His head. In that moment you know that, despite your fears, you must sign up. God, through prayer, has just rearranged your priorities.

Questions:
• What is one thing God has said to you in your prayer times recently?

_____

_____

• What are you doing as a result?

_____

_____

God Speaks to You Through Circumstances

A third way the Holy Spirit speaks to you is through the everyday events of your life. The Holy Spirit was convicting a college student named Tyrone about his need to tithe his earnings from his job to his local church. Every cent was precious but the Spirit persisted. Finally, during a service at his church, Tyrone placed $40.00 in the offering plate. As he was leaving the church, a fellow student approached him and said God had impressed her to give him a card. At home, Tyrone opened the card to find four ten-dollar bills! Through circumstances in this student's life, God spoke loud and clear!

Read carefully the Scriptures to the right that describe how God speaks to you through your circumstances.

Questions:
• In John 5, how did Jesus determine His Father's will for His life?

_____

_____

• Who is the only person, according to John 14:6, who knows the entire "truth" of your circumstances?

_____

• How does Romans 8:28 indicate we should look at even our worst circumstances?

_____

_____

_____

Circumstances can be wonderful opportunities for God to speak to you. Jesus said in John 5 that He never did anything on His own initiative. He always observed the events around Him in order to recognize God at work. When He saw God working, Jesus adjusted His life and joined Him. Jesus told His disciples in John 14:6 that He was the "truth." This means that only He can reveal what the truth of your circumstances is. Romans 8:28 says there will never be a situation in your life where God cannot speak to you and bring something good into your life.

"I tell you the truth, the Son can do nothing by himself; he can do only what he sees his Father doing, because whatever the Father does the Son also does. For the Father loves the Son and shows him all he does."
John 5:19-20a

"Jesus said, 'I am the way and the truth and the life. No one comes to the Father except through me.'"
John 14:6

"And we know that in all things God works for the good of those who love him, who have been called according to his purpose."
Romans 8:28

• How have you heard God speaking to you through your circumstances recently?

_____

• What have you done as a result?

_____

"So in Christ we who are many form one body, and each member belongs to all the others." **Romans 12:5**

"Now to each one the manifestation of the Spirit is given for the common good." **1 Corinthians 12:7**

"It was he who gave some to be apostles, some to be prophets, some to be evangelists, and some to be pastors and teachers, to prepare God's people for works of service, so that the body of Christ may be built up until we all reach unity in the faith and in the knowledge of the Son of God and become mature, attaining to the whole measure of the fullness of Christ." **Ephesians 4:11-13**

God Speaks to You Through the Church

Often God speaks to you through another Christian. A college minister told the story about a student named Cheryl who visited his office. Cheryl related her financial problems and asked: "Do you think God could help me find a job?" The minister assured her that He could and began to tell of times when God had provided for him. While he spoke, a student poked her head in the office and said, "Hey Cheryl, I'm glad I caught you! Listen, when you get finished here I need to see you. A position has opened up where I work and I wanted to recommend you. I need to talk to you about it." Cheryl assured her she would and then turned to the college minister and asked in the same desperate voice she had begun their conversation with: "So, do you *really* think God could provide me a job?" God will speak to you through the people of God. Be sensitive to His voice when He does!

Notice in the Scriptures to the left what God says He will do through the local church.

Questions:
• Where does God place you when you become a Christian?

_____

• Why does the Holy Spirit manifest Himself to you?

_____

• How and why does God equip members in the church?

_____

_____

A church is a living body of Christ and each member helps all the others grow to completeness in Christ (Ephesians 4:7, 11-16). When you are an active member in a local church, God will speak clearly to you through the other members of the church family. The Holy Spirit will manifest Himself in your life in order to encourage others in the church toward Christian maturity.

Questions:
• How has God spoken to you through your church recently?

_____

_____

• What did God say to you during your study today?

_____

_____

_____

• What will you do as a result?

_____

_____

_____

LESSON 3
God Follows a Pattern

As a young man, D.L. Moody was well on his way to becoming a successful business-man. He had the natural ability and ambition to go to the top. Then a man named Henry Varley challenged Moody by saying: "This world has yet to see what God can do with a man fully consecrated to Him." The Holy Spirit used these words to burn deeply into Moody's soul. Speaking to Varley later, Moody revealed: "Those were the words sent to my soul, through you, from the living God. As I crossed the wide Atlantic, the boards of the deck of the vessel were engraved with them, and when I reached Chicago, the very paving stones seemed marked with 'Moody, the world has yet to see what God will do with a man fully consecrated to Him.'"

Moody ultimately responded to God with the prayer, "By God's help I aim to be that man." God was doing more than just issuing a challenge to a young man, for He knew what He could make of Moody and how He could use his life. God, through the challenge of Henry Varley, was inviting Moody to join Him in HIS activity rather than to continue pursuing his own goals. So mightily did God use Moody, it is estimated that over one hundred million people heard him preach during his ministry; three schools were formed; two Christian publishing houses were begun; and a student mission movement that included some of the greatest missionaries in modern history was inspired. Since Moody's death, his writings and influence continue to win millions of people to God. Moody could never have dreamed of all that God wanted to do through his life, yet when he heard Him speak, he responded to the invitation.

The Disciple John

God will relate to you in a manner that is unique and personal. Throughout Scripture there is a general pattern which God used as He invited men and women to join in His eternal activity. John the Apostle could serve as a model of this pattern. *Notice in the passage to the right the simplicity of Jesus' invitation.*

In John's life there are five realities which can guide you as you look to see how God involves you in His work.

1. God is always at work around you.

Since the beginning of creation God had been planning to send a Savior to earth to save His people from their sins. God promised Abraham that through his descendants

> "As Jesus walked beside the Sea of Galilee, he saw Simon and his brother Andrew casting a net into the lake, for they were fishermen. 'Come, follow me,' Jesus said, 'and I will make you fishers of men.' At once they left their nets and followed him. When he had gone a little farther, he saw James son of Zebedee and his brother John in a boat, preparing their nets. Without delay he called them, and they left their father Zebedee in the boat with the hired men and followed him."
>
> **Mark 1:16-20**

all the nations of the earth would be blessed (Genesis 22:18). King David also anticipated the Savior's arrival (Psalm 22, 110). Great prophets such as Isaiah spoke of the time of the Messiah's coming (Isaiah 7:14; 9:1-7; 53). And now, during John's lifetime, while the mighty Roman Empire seemed invincible and at a time when the Jewish nation was defeated, God's eternal plan was culminating in the coming of His Son Jesus. As Jesus walked in the region of Galilee, people were unaware of the staggering reality that the Son of God Himself was talking to them face to face. From a human perspective, God's people had been defeated by the dreaded Romans. From God's perspective, His activity continued as He had determined, unhindered by men. From a human perspective, the Roman Empire had created intricate roads, fortresses, armies and a navy that ensured theirs was the most significant power in the world. From God's perspective, the Romans had been unknowing instruments of His plan: preparing a safe and extensive travel network upon which missionaries could take His good news around the world.

2. God loves you and invites you to become involved with Him in His work.

John was a young man, the son of a fisherman, when he first met Jesus. His father, Zebedee, wanted him to carry on the family business. A religious education had never been considered. John was fortunate, for he was inheriting a business that was apparently successful, considering he had partners as well as servants. Had John spent his life as a fisherman on the tiny Sea of Galilee, he would have died virtually unknown.

God loved John and invited him to join in His work (Mark 3:14). John would be a friend who savored Jesus' company and whose fellowship Jesus enjoyed. John was receiving an invitation to walk with the Son of God. It is more significant to be a fisher of men than a fisher of fish! God was unfolding His eternal plan and John was to have a part in it. Jesus knew all that John's life could become. John knew only that he should respond to Jesus' invitation.

3. God speaks to you by His Holy Spirit through the Bible, prayer, circumstances, and the church.

John had the singular opportunity to hear Jesus' voice and to look Him in the face. When Jesus said, "Come, follow me," John left his career and immediately followed Jesus. When he was sent out to preach in the surrounding villages, John went. When Jesus had special times of prayer with His closest disciples, John participated. Whenever Jesus spoke, it was an invitation for John to believe God and to be obedient. The time for Jesus to speak to His followers in this manner, however, lasted only a few short years. As Jesus was preparing to leave the disciples in His physical form, He promised John and the other disciples: *"The Counselor, the Holy Spirit, whom the Father will send in my name, will teach you all things and will remind you of everything I have said to you" (John 14:26).* Although Jesus would no longer relate to John as an earthly man, He would send the Holy Spirit who would open John's understanding to what the heavenly Father was saying through the Bible, prayer, circumstances, and the church.

Jesus assured John that whenever he read the Scriptures, the Holy Spirit would

1. God is always at work around you.

2. God loves you and invites you to become involved with Him in His work.

3. God speaks to you by His Holy Spirit through the Bible, prayer, circumstances, and the church.

4. God's invitation will create a crisis of belief which will require you to make adjustments in your life.

5. When you obey, you experience God's power working through you and you bring Him glory.

"guide you into all truth" (John 16:13). Furthermore, when John prayed, the Holy Spirit would be present to help him understand what God was saying to him. It appears that John was praying when he saw his amazing apocalypse on the Isle of Patmos (Revelation 1:10). John was encouraged that he would never face a situation in his life where the Holy Spirit was not present to help him understand and learn from his circumstances (John 14:18). Finally, John came to understand that it was in the context of the local church that believers could encounter the risen Christ in a profound way (Revelation 3:20).

4. God's invitation will create a crisis of belief which will require you to make adjustments in your life.

When Jesus invited John to join in His activity, it created a crisis of belief for John. That is, although John believed in God, he was now being asked to do an impossible task. This is the difference between head knowledge and faith in God. John was not trained to be a religious leader or teacher. He was trained to catch fish. Now Jesus was asking him to leave what he knew to do something unfamiliar. John was still a young man and probably not old enough to garner much respect as a teacher or preacher in his community. Furthermore, John's father, Zebedee, would be left behind. We can only speculate if John, as he followed Jesus, did not cast a painful look back at his father still in their boat.

John's character was not conducive to being a church leader. He had a hot temper which prompted Jesus to nickname him a "Son of Thunder" (Mark 3:17). When a Samaritan village did not welcome Jesus, John and his brother James offered to call down fire from heaven to destroy the inhospitable villagers (Luke 9:54). Not only was John prone to anger, but he was pursuing his personal ambition. John and his brother dared to approach Jesus to ask if they might have the two highest places of honor in Jesus' kingdom (Mark 10:35-41). Being probably the youngest disciple, this showed strong ambition and a willingness to get the better of others in order to gain personal advantage. These character flaws in John made his becoming a world-changing, church-planting, Scripture-writing apostle an impossible feat in human terms. Fortunately for John, Jesus not only invited him to attempt the impossible but also developed his character until he was the kind of man to whom He would entrust God-sized assignments.

5. When you obey, you experience God's power working through you and you bring Him glory.

Despite John's shaky beginnings, he came to understand that each time he obeyed Christ, God worked through him and received glory. After John received the Holy Spirit, he experienced the incredible joy of being used by God to bring salvation to others. While John and Peter were on their way to the temple, they encountered a man who had been lame all his life. When they healed the man, he experienced salvation. A crowd soon gathered and listened to the Gospel (Acts 3). As a result of their witness, many believed and the church grew to over 5,000 men (Acts 4:4). Peter and John were used by God so significantly that Acts notes: *"When they saw the courage of Peter and John and realized that they were unschooled, ordinary men, they were astonished and they took note that these men had been with Jesus" (Acts 4:13).* So filled with the Spirit were John and his com-

> God will relate to you in a manner that is unique and personal. Throughout Scripture there is a general pattern which God used as He invited men and women to join in His eternal activity.

100

50

0

panions that: *"The place where they were meeting was shaken . . . . With great power the apostles continued to testify to the resurrection of the Lord Jesus, and much grace was upon them all"* (Acts 4:31, 33).

John wrote the Gospel of John, First, Second and Third John as well as the book of Revelation. These letters would be read, preached, taught, and studied in every language around the world. Surely John did not imagine that God would choose to use a fisherman to be part of such an enormous work! The more John obeyed, however, the more God involved him in His work, and the greater the glory God received through John's life.

Questions:

• List the five realities of God's invitation in the space to the left.

• Is God presently inviting you to become involved with Him in His activity? What is He inviting you to do?

_____

• Which reality of God's invitation are you presently experiencing?

_____

• How are you responding to God's invitation?

_____

_____

• What did God say to you during your study today?

_____

_____

• What will you do as a result?

_____

LESSON 4
God Invites Us to an Intimate Relationship

During the time I served as pastor, I had the privilege of performing the weddings of many college students and would counsel with them during the weeks leading up to their wedding. There was always a glow about them as they excitedly prepared for their future together. I remember a couple that came to my home for premarital counseling. They spoke of the plans they had and the arrangements they were making for their wedding. I directed a question at the woman: "Do you love this man and are you willing to commit yourself to him for the rest of your life?" After a pause, she confessed she did not really love him! She did not want to invest her life with him. They had both been so enamored with the idea of having a wedding, receiving gifts, building a home and family, that they had ignored the fact that they did not have a relationship of love. They realized that it would be wrong to marry without such a commitment and they broke their engagement.

College students do not get married just so they can perform household chores, provide for a family, or cook meals. They get married because they are in love! In the same way, the Christian life is not merely a set of activities. College students do not become Christians just so they can go to church every Sunday, read their Bible daily, and give money to the church! They become Christians because they come to love Jesus Christ. Christianity is a RELATIONSHIP. It is NOT a set of doctrines to believe, duties to perform, sins to avoid, or rituals to practice. Christianity is a relationship with a Person who loves you more than you will ever comprehend and who wants you to love Him in return.

Jesus described the essence of the Christian life when he prayed: *"Now this is eternal life: that they may know you, the only true God, and Jesus Christ whom you have sent" (John 17:3).* According to Jesus, eternal life is knowing God. This is not just a head knowledge, or the collection of facts *about* God, but an intimate, growing, deepening relationship.

The Apostle John had the pleasure of coming to know Jesus in this way. *In the Scripture to the right, notice the wonderful relationship that Jesus developed with John. Go back and underline each act or statement that indicates a friendship between Jesus and John.*

Did you notice the way John referred to himself when he wrote his gospel? Modesty prevented him from mentioning his own name and so at times he used a designation for himself. He could have referred to himself as "the one who believed in God" or, "the one who followed Jesus." Instead, he thought of himself in terms of his relationship with Jesus: "the one whom Jesus loved." What a profound way to look at yourself!

Question:
In the boxes below, check the descriptions which best describe your relationship with God:

- ❏ intimate and personal
- ❏ a true friendship
- ❏ broken relationship
- ❏ one whom Jesus loves

- ❏ distant
- ❏ seldom talk
- ❏ have little in common
- ❏ beginning friendship

- ❏ growing
- ❏ cold and stale
- ❏ strangers

Throughout the Scriptures God is presented as someone who seeks to have a love-relationship with people. God called Abraham His friend (Isaiah 41:8), and Scripture says God spoke to Moses *"face to face, as a man speaks with his friend" (Exodus 33:11).*

Questions:
• In the space to the right, list two things you are doing to enhance your love relationship with God. If you cannot do this, list one activity you *could* do to improve your relationship.

"One of them, the disciple whom Jesus loved, was reclining next to him. Simon Peter motioned to this disciple and said, 'Ask him which one he means.' Leaning back against Jesus, he asked him, 'Lord, who is it?'" **John 13:23-25**

"When Jesus saw his mother there, and the disciple whom he loved standing nearby, he said to his mother, 'Dear woman, here is your son,' and to the disciple, 'Here is your mother.' From that time on, this disciple took her into his home." **John 19:26-27**

"Then the disciple whom Jesus loved said to Peter, 'It is the Lord!'" **John 21:7**

"No one will be able to stand up against you all the days of your life. As I was with Moses, so I will be with you; I will never leave you nor forsake you. Be strong and courageous, because you will lead these people to inherit the land I swore to their forefathers to give them. Be strong and very courageous. Be careful to obey all the law my servant Moses gave you; do not turn from it to the right or to the left, that you may be successful wherever you go. Do not let this Book of the Law depart from your mouth; meditate on it day and night, so that you may be careful to do everything written in it. Then you will be prosperous and successful. Have I not commanded you? Be strong and courageous. Do not be terrified; do not be discouraged, for the Lord your God will be with you wherever you go."

Joshua 1:5-9

• Is your relationship with God presently broken? Do you need to repent of anything in order to restore this relationship? If so, what is it? Jot it down.

Joshua's Invitation

Read the invitation God gave to Joshua in the Sciptue to the left and underline the words or phrases that indicate a relationship between God and Joshua.

Questions:

• Go back and circle the phrases which indicate what Joshua was told to do.

• What was the connection between Joshua's relationship with God and his assignment from God?

_____

God works through His people on the basis of His relationship with them. Joshua was given an assignment, but it could only be carried out if he maintained his relationship with God. As Joshua obeyed God's instructions and meditated on His word, God promised He would not leave Joshua and would give him success wherever he went. What an awesome invitation! Joshua's primary responsibility was to maintain his relationship with God, not to perform as a good general or a model administrator.

Questions:

• What is God presently leading you to *do* as a result of your relationship with Him?

_____

• Is there something you are presently attempting to do for God out of your own strength and not out of your relationship with God? If so, what is it?

_____

• What did God say to you in your study today?

_____

• What will you do as a result?

_____

LESSON 5
God Calls to a Definite Choice
A Wasted Life

When I was a pastor many college students stood before the church to say they felt God leading them to train for full-time Christian service. Most of them went on to seminary or Bible college. One young man indicated God was speaking to him about becoming a pastor. He was a talented fellow, a gifted athlete and musician who was doing well in university. He volunteered for summer missions and served in a pioneer church for several weeks. He returned so excited about how God had used him during that summer! Then, he had to decide whether or not to leave our city and travel to a distant seminary for his ministerial training. While deliberating, he was offered a great chance to use his musical ability. He decided to delay going to seminary in order to pursue several of his other interests. He entered a business enterprise and it wasn't long before talk of preparing for the ministry ceased. One day, a couple of years later, he was killed in a freak accident on the job. I do not know what God had in store for this man but I sense that this life was tragically cut short before God could bring about His best.

God wants to give you abundant life (John 10:10b). However, He will not force His best upon you. To accept what the world provides rather than what God offers you is called "death" in Scripture. It means missing out on what God has in store for you. This may result in a lack of peace and fulfillment. It can mean anxiety, broken relationships, and mediocrity, or even death. God speaks to His people, setting before them HIS ways. The choice then is between: life (good) versus death (evil).

Read Deuteronomy 30:11-20 and identify the two choices and the two consequences God's people had to choose:

Choice #1   **Choice #2**

_____   _____

Consequence #1   **Consequence #2**

_____   _____

Questions:

• According to this passage, how difficult is it for you to know God's will?

_____

• When God speaks, what are your choices?

_____

• What happens if you do not protect your relationship with God?

_____

Investments for a Lifetime

I had a university student share with me that he was struggling between two directions for his life. On the one hand he felt God had called him into full-time Christian ministry. He had been invited to lead a new Christian student group on campus. On the other hand, he had a burning desire to become a millionaire. He felt certain that through real estate he could become wealthy at a young age. He reasoned that with his wealth he could support many Christian causes. He chose to pursue his fortune. Everything went according to his plan until the real estate market crashed. He lost everything, including his family. He had chosen to invest in the temporal rather than the eternal and he discovered how transitory the things of this world are.

Life is full of choices. The issue of how much of your life you will spend is already settled: twenty-four hours each day. How you spend it is another matter. How you respond to the invitations God gives you will determine the kind and quality of your life.

> God wants to give you abundant life (John 10:10b). However, He will not force His best upon you. To accept what the world provides rather than what God offers you is called "death" in Scripture.

100

50

0

"Do not store up for yourselves treasures on earth, where moth and rust destroy, and where thieves break in and steal. But store up for yourselves treasures in heaven, where moth and rust do not destroy, and where thieves do not break in and steal."
Matthew 6:19-20

"The ground of a certain rich man produced a good crop. He thought to himself, 'What shall I do? I have no place to store my crops.' Then he said, 'This is what I'll do. I will tear down my barns and build bigger ones and there I will store all my grain and my goods. And I'll say to myself, 'You have plenty of good things laid up for many years. Take life easy; eat, drink and be merry.' But God said to him, 'You fool! This very night your life will be demanded from you. Then who will get what you have prepared for yourself?' This is how it will be with anyone who stores up things for himself but is not rich toward God."
Luke 12:16-21

In the Scripture to the left, notice what Jesus said about how you can invest your life. In the space below list what Jesus said to invest in and what the rich fool invested in:

JESUS' TEACHING	RICH FOOL

Jesus said to store up for yourself "treasures in heaven." That is, invest your life in things which have eternal value and will not pass away with time. Spiritual things do not suffer decay as do physical things. To lead someone to a personal relationship with Jesus Christ would mean that their eternity was immediately altered and a place in heaven would be prepared as a result of what you had done on earth.

In contrast, the Rich Fool had made no preparation for eternity. Perhaps he planned to do so once his earthly concerns were dealt with but, since he did not have God's eternal perspective, he was oblivious to the fact that his life was about to come to an unexpected end. He had done what society praises. He had worked hard, harvested a good crop and stored his grain. His barns were full and there was not enough room to store all of his possessions. He expanded his operation so that he had enormous reserves of grain and goods. Now he could enjoy early retirement in ease and luxury. There was nothing wrong or evil about planning for his retirement, except that he had not first prepared for eternity. If he had known that his life was to end soon, surely he would have ordered his priorities differently! That is why it is critical that as a student you allow God to guide you in the way you invest your life. Only He knows what lies ahead and how you can lay up treasures for yourself which will make you rich toward God.

Questions:

• What is one way you are tempted to invest your life in temporal rather than eternal things. _____

• How could this keep you from experiencing God's best?
_____

• What changes do you need to make in the way you are investing your life?
_____

• What did God say to you during your study today?
_____

• What will you do as a result?
_____

[1]Mrs. Howard Taylor, *Borden of Yale: The Life that Counts,* (Philadelphia: China Inland Mission, 1926; reprinted., 1957).

INTRODUCTION

Daniel was a young man with a promising future. He had done well in school and now powerful people were vying for his services. Moving far from home, he found himself surrounded by every imaginable temptation. Daniel had been raised in a religious home with strict morals and values. Now influential people were telling him that if he would compromise just a little, he could obtain wealth and power beyond his wildest dreams! It seemed as though he had everything to gain and nothing to lose. To refuse to go along could seriously harm his future. The potential for success seemed enormous; the possibility of being caught, remote. What would you do?

Of course we know what Daniel chose to do. The Bible reveals that despite all the temptations and threats he received, *"Daniel resolved not to defile himself" (Daniel 1:8).* What amazing integrity! He did not need his parents looking over his shoulder or his hometown pastor checking up on him; he had developed a spiritual strength of character so firm that even the most tantalizing temptations could not shake his convictions. Do you have that kind of integrity before God and with people?

LESSON 1
Our Function: An Assignment Based on Character

Newspapers occasionally report on lawyers who betray their clients' trust and illegally use money not their own. Others bill their clients falsely or mishandle trust funds. The paradox is that these are the same people who have spent years carefully studying the laws of their land. Apparently for some, their goal has been simply to obtain a job with wealth and prestige. Their studies obviously had no effect on their character.

In God's eyes, not just the end is important but the journey to the end as well. The activities of our lives are God's means for helping change us into what He wants us to be. Jesus told John, *"Come, follow me . . . and I will make you . . ." (Mark 1:17).* Jesus told John He would transform him into a fisher of men if he would follow Him as a disciple. God is not as concerned with our activities as He is with our character which motivates our actions.

When God revealed Himself to the Israelites while they were slaves in Egypt, He did so for a purpose. He rescued them from slavery and brought them to Himself so they might enjoy freedom as God's people. *Read in Exodus 19:5-6 what God wanted to do with His people.*

MEMORY VERSE:

"Above all else, guard your heart, for it is the wellspring of life."

Proverbs 4:23

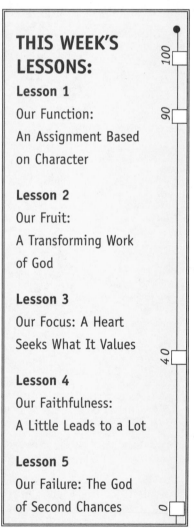

THIS WEEK'S LESSONS:

Lesson 1
Our Function: An Assignment Based on Character

Lesson 2
Our Fruit: A Transforming Work of God

Lesson 3
Our Focus: A Heart Seeks What It Values

Lesson 4
Our Faithfulness: A Little Leads to a Lot

Lesson 5
Our Failure: The God of Second Chances

Questions:

• What did God want for His people based on Exodus 19:5-6?

_____

_____

• In the same passage, what did the Israelites have to do to be what God wanted?

_____

_____

God, out of His grace, chose to make the Israelites His "treasured possession." He wanted to make them a "kingdom of priests and a holy nation." There would never be another nation like this. This rag-tag collection of uneducated, demoralized slaves was going to become a unique group. Every person would have a special relationship with God and would be His ambassador to the world. God was going to accomplish this by making a commitment to them and giving them careful instructions about how to live in order to be acceptable to Him.

Character Dictates Conduct

What you are made of determines how you act. Trustworthy individuals are elevated to positions of responsibility. On the contrary, people in authority can fall, losing everything because of a serious character flaw. In Scripture, the core of your personality is commonly referred to as the "heart." This is where you make moral decisions and hold values. Your spontaneous actions reveal your inner self. For example, if you automatically tell the truth, then you are by nature a truthful person. However, if you sometimes struggle with telling the truth as you consider what would benefit you the most, then you are *not* an honest person. You have a serious flaw that could ultimately lead to ruin. What you do instinctively in *any* situation *is* your character. Jesus was far more concerned with people's hearts than He was with their actions. Notice His observation in Luke 6:43-45.

Questions:

• According to Jesus, how do you recognize different trees?

_____

_____

• How can you identify a "good tree"?

_____

_____

• Where do your actions come from?

_____

• Is it possible to be a "good" tree and produce "bad" fruit?

_____

_____

Jesus taught that a tree is identified by the fruit it produces. Likewise, students may claim to be one thing but the "fruit" of their lives will shout the opposite.

Read the Scripture to the right and notice the things Jesus said were incompatible in a person's life.

Questions:
• In the verses in Luke 6:43-45, list practices or attitudes that cannot be part of a Christlike character.

• Now go back and look for any trait that is presently part of your character. How would you describe your character in light of these verses?

_____

_____

Do you see the importance of your heart's condition? If your heart is right and your character is Christlike, certain actions will naturally occur and others will be noticeably absent.

Whether at work or at church, most students like to feel that their peers or superiors have enough confidence to entrust them with an important job. With God, ANY task He gives you is significant! However, God is far more concerned with your character than He is with your assignment.

Here is some thought-provoking counsel given by others.

"Do not pray for easy lives, pray to be stronger men. Do not pray for tasks equal to your powers, pray for powers equal to your tasks. Then the doing of your work shall be no miracle, but you shall be a miracle." Phillips Brooks, *Twenty Sermons*, 330.

"Men are God's method. The church is looking for better methods; God is looking for better men." E.M. Bounds, *Power Through Prayer*, 5.

"If your place is not great enough to suit you, make it so. The minister who is unable to make a place great is too weak to hold a great one." L.R. Scarborough, *With Christ After the Lost*, 79.

No Shortcuts to Character
God assigns tasks according to what He sees in your heart. Right now, how big would God's assignment be for you?

Do you know students whose primary focus is to find the easiest path to their goal? They pick classes based on who the least demanding professor is. They find short-

"Why do you call me, 'Lord, Lord,' and do not do what I say?" **Luke 6:46**

"No one who is born of God will continue to sin, because God's seed remains in him; he cannot go on sinning, because he has been born of God." **1 John 3:9**

"Anyone who hates his brother is a murderer, and you know that no murderer has eternal life in him." **1 John 3:15**

"If anyone has material possessions and sees his brother in need but has no pity on him, how can the love of God be in him?" **1 John 3:17**

"If we claim to have fellowship with him yet walk in the darkness, we lie and do not live by the truth." **1 John 1:6**

"Do not love the world or anything in the world. If anyone loves the world, the love of the Father is not in him." **1 John 2:15**

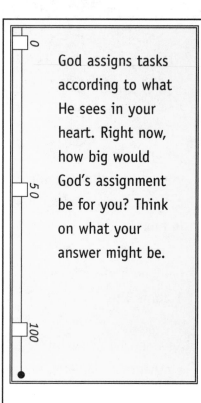

God assigns tasks according to what He sees in your heart. Right now, how big would God's assignment be for you? Think on what your answer might be.

cuts to studying; if they can pass with a "C," they do not strive for an "A." Some students even pay others to write their papers.

This approach shortchanges them in skills, knowledge, and personal growth that will affect God's future assignment for them. I can't tell you how many people have come to me in great frustration, sharing how they were careless with their studies in university or seminary because they were simply pushing to get through and find a job. Then God began speaking to them about His plans for them. In response, they applied to various programs and schools only to discover that their grade-point average was too low or they had bypassed difficult required classes and now the door was closed. They had not "become" all they should and now their future assignments from God were limited.

Further, this kind of student is often quick to abandon his studies when a tempting offer comes along. I have known students who were offered jobs while still in school. In their eagerness to "jump to the finish line," they dropped out of school, telling themselves, "I don't need to keep studying. I have a job now!" Many times their "careers" end in failure, partly because they had inadequate training. An additional reason, however, is their character. It is such that they jump at every new and seemingly easier opportunity that comes along and therefore they never give God the time to build into them the strength that can withstand the difficult tests that were sure to come.

Questions:

• Is God presently giving you a "big" assignment? If so, what is it? If not, why do you think He is not? Jot your answers in the space at the left.

• What area of your character is God presently working on?

_____

• What did God say to you during your study today?

_____

_____

• What will you do as a result?

_____

LESSON 2
Our Fruit: A Transforming Work of God

In 1463 the sculptor, Agostino di Duccio was commissioned to produce a statue. He was given a large slab of marble upon which he began to chisel out his masterpiece. Tragically, however, his apprentice made a careless mistake which left the marble disfigured. Agostino was horrified at the sight of the damaged stone and did everything in his power to restore it, yet to no avail. This beautiful, unfinished marble with such potential was declared hopelessly ruined. Rejected by its master, the rock stood in a courtyard for the next 38 years.

In 1501 a 25 year-old artist named Michaelangelo came upon the abandoned stone. When he looked at the marble he did not see a broken piece of rock, but incredible potential. All he had to do was chisel away anything that did not look like a masterpiece. When he was done, there stood the awesome, "Statue of David," one of the greatest sculptures of all time!

Some students arrive on campus "broken" and "scarred." Perhaps a difficult home life or a painful event in their past has left them damaged or incomplete. They may bear the stains of past sins they committed or were committed against them. There may be scars that run deeply as a result of a sinful lifestyle. The good news is that Christ wants to help you BECOME someone only God could create.

Peter the Rock

It is interesting to see how Jesus gave some of His disciples "nicknames" to illustrate their character. He named Simon, "Peter," meaning "rock." I imagine you have heard the expression "steady as a rock"; well, Peter's early career as a disciple was anything but steady! Nevertheless, Jesus took Peter through a process of character development that was extremely thorough.

Contrast the following passages that reflect growth in Peter's character over time as he walked with Jesus.

BEFORE	AFTER
Read Matthew 14:29-31. Read Luke 22:60-62.	Read Acts 12:6-11. Read Acts 4:13, 18-20.

Questions:

• What changes do you notice in the character of Peter?

_____

• Is there one area of your character you feel God has changed? What is it?

_____

• What aspect(s) of your character do you think Jesus would like to change?

_____

As a new convert, Peter was sincere, but suffered a shallow faith. He was willing to impulsively step out on the water to meet Jesus but as soon as he realized what he had done, he began to doubt. Later, he trusted God so completely he slept soundly the night before his scheduled execution and escaped a maximum security prison without expressing the slightest doubt! As a new convert, Peter was someone who crumbled under pressure. When a servant girl asked him if he was a disciple of Jesus, Peter became so fearful he denied it, cursing. Later, under the fiercest threats by the most powerful men in the nation, he stood firm in his loyalty to Christ.

The difference was Christ and the changes He made in Peter's character. When

Jesus met Peter He saw beyond what he was like at that moment to what Peter could become by the transforming work of the Spirit of God. While it is true that Christ loves you just the way you are, He also loves you DESPITE the way you are. If God accepted you without expecting you to change, that would not be genuine love. Christ loves you and is determined to make you reach your full potential as a Spirit-filled child of God. As Christ develops your character, the Heavenly Father will continue to expand your assignment.

Paul the Pharisee

The Apostle Paul experienced the reality that Christ can take the most hardened sinner and transform him into a saint. *In the Scripture to the left, notice what he said about himself.*

Questions:
• List things you notice that reflect Paul's character before he became a Christian.

_____

_____

• If you had known Paul at that time, would you have thought it likely that he would become a devout Christian leader and church starter? Why or why not?

_____

_____

"For you have heard of my previous way of life in Judaism, how intensely I persecuted the church of God and tried to destroy it. I was advancing in Judaism beyond many Jews of my own age and was extremely zealous for the traditions of my fathers."
Galatians 1:13-14

"Therefore, if anyone is in Christ, he is a new creation; the old has gone, the new has come!"
2 Corinthians 5:17

Paul was a sanctimonious Pharisee. He was fiercely competitive and strived to surpass his peers in his religious zeal. He callously imprisoned Christians and had some put to death. Paul saw nothing wrong with his character and felt he was living a faultless life. He was ambitiously using the system to advance his career and reach the pinnacle of power among his people. This was NOT the kind of person you expect to become a Christian martyr, let alone invite home for dinner! *Yet notice the change Christ brought about in his life as illustrated in exerpts from Paul's letters in the sidebars.*

Questions:
• Below 2 Corinthians 5:17, list the changes you detect in the character of Paul.

• What did Paul say was the reason for his change of character?

_____

Few lives mentioned in Scripture underwent as dramatic a turnaround as Paul's. Christ transformed him into someone totally different from what he had been. Paul's life became a miracle of God's grace.

You will never be able to develop a Christlike character on your own. Despite all your best efforts, and all the self-help books you might read, only Christ can produce a Christlike character. This is accomplished as the Holy Spirit works in your life.

Read the following fruits of the Spirit from Galatians 5:22-24. Write down one example of the Holy Spirit's activity in your life in each area.

love: _____

joy: _____

patience: _____

kindness:_____

goodness: _____

faithfulness: _____

gentleness: _____

self-control: _____

• What do you notice about what God is doing in your character?

_____

The Holy Spirit is determined to produce spiritual fruit in your life. He will not *force* you to love or to be joyful, but if you allow Him, He will mold you and remove harmful things from your life until, when He is finished, your character resembles that of Christ.

• What did God say to you during your study today?

_____

_____

• What will you do as a result?

_____

_____

LESSON 3
Our Focus: A Heart Seeks What It Values

While I was a pastor, our college students annually held a spring banquet. This was always a special time for the students, and everyone came dressed in their finest attire. One year, a slovenly stranger wandered into the banquet room and began visiting with the college students. He obviously was not one of the group, and he began to make people uncomfortable. When the meal was served, the intruder found a seat and began eating with the others. The students did what they could to let this young man know that this was a private function, but he was undaunted.

After the meal a skit was performed. The sketch began with a scene in heaven in which God summoned an angel to go and investigate OUR college group. Suddenly this stranger appeared! He was the angel! He had been enlisted by the student president to test his reception by the rest of the group. Many felt embarrassed at the way they had been cold and unfriendly to the stranger. Although the students took pride

"But the fruit of the Spirit is love, joy, peace, patience, kindness, goodness, faithfulness, gentleness and self-control. Against such things there is no law. Those who belong to Christ Jesus have crucified the sinful nature with its passions and desires. Since we live by the Spirit, let us keep in step with the Spirit. Let us not become conceited, provoking and envying each other." **Galatians 5:22-26**

"Being confident of this, that he who began a good work in you will carry it on to completion until the day of Christ Jesus."
Philippians 1:6

> "Above all else, guard your heart, for it is the wellspring of life. Put away perversity from your mouth; keep corrupt talk far from your lips. Let your eyes look straight ahead, fix your gaze directly before you. Make level paths for your feet and take only ways that are firm. Do not swerve to the right or the left; keep your foot from evil." **Proverbs 4:23-27**

in their friendliness, on this occasion, when they were tested, they had failed the test!

How you respond in unguarded moments can be the best test of your character. Unexpected temptation can be devastating! You may think you have a holy life or that you are a loving person but when the test comes, if you are unprepared, you may discover the true nature of your heart. *Heed the wise advice of the writer of Proverbs in the Scripture to the left.*

Questions:

• In your own words, in the space alloted to the left list the things you are instructed to do.

• Go back and circle those things you are presently doing.

There are at least three things that greatly affect your character. These are your values, friends, and habits. Consider the following carefully.

Values: Keeping You on Track

I remember a young couple who had dedicated their lives to full-time Christian service. They entered school to train for the ministry they knew God was calling them to. Since they both had jobs while they were in school, they decided a house would be a wise investment. They began acquiring furniture and appliances for their new home. Then they purchased a second car. The need to earn more money to pay their bills grew greater and first one, and then the other, dropped out of school. The stress of trying to run the rat race of consumerism was so great that their marriage grew shaky. What happened? Instead of sticking to their priority of obeying God and finishing their education, they had allowed material possessions to become their top priority and almost lost everything.

Jesus said, *"For where your treasure is, there your heart will be also"* (Matthew 6:21). That is, those things which are most important to you will be what you give the majority of your time, money, and energy to. The things your heart treasures are your values. During your college years you will establish values that will shape and determine your future. The challenge will be to place the utmost importance on God and what He wants for your life as opposed to the possessions, activities, and rewards the world offers. You need an "undivided heart" for the things of God. This means that you do not highly merit the things of God AND the things of the world. Jesus said that if you *"seek first his kingdom and his righteousness, . . . all these things will be given to you as well"* *(Matthew 6:33).* That is, when your values are the same as God's, He will grant you many of those lesser things as well.

Notice the contrast in the values of the Rich Young Ruler, the woman, and the disciples. Take your Bible and read Luke 18:18-24 and Matthew 26:6-9.

Questions:

• What did the Rich Ruler "value" more than anything else? How do you know?

_____

• How did Jesus deal with the young man who had values different from His own?

_____

_____

• What was important to the woman? How can you tell?

_____

• What was important to the disciples? How can you tell?

_____

The Rich Ruler professed to be devoted to God and His causes. Yet, in his heart, he was really dedicated to his money. Jesus saw through the pretense of devotion and asked the man to rid himself of that which had a higher value than following Him. This radical command by Jesus laid bare the man's true values so that Jesus and everyone listening could see what was the real treasure of his heart.

The woman treasured Jesus and her relationship with Him more than anything. Her most precious possession was easily poured out in exchange for being able to express her love to Jesus. The disciples, however, were still bound by a worldly set of values. They knew it was good to show affection for Jesus, but they also knew the cost of this expensive perfume. Here was the battle of values being waged between what the world esteems and what is supremely important to God!

The reason your values are important is that they determine your actions. You may have two job offers upon graduation. One job may afford you the time to invest in your family and volunteer at your church. The other may pay a much higher salary but require you to travel and have little time for anything but work. The values you hold will strongly influence which job you take. You may be faced with the opportunity to have an affair with a married person. If your primary value is: "have a good time at all costs," you will succumb to the temptation. If your value is: "maintain moral purity and commitments made to your spouse," you will resist any activity that might make you compromise. You will even avoid the *appearance* of compromise. Without God-given values, your life will be adrift in an ocean of loose morals and questionable values.

Question:
• What is God saying to you about the values you presently hold?

_____

_____

Your Friends: A Subtle Influence
While I was a pastor I had a young man tell me that he was "witnessing" to some friends every Saturday night. He said they loved to spend the evening working on and racing their cars. He told me he thought he was really having a positive influence on his friends. I asked him what difference he thought he was making. I noted that I had

"Blessed is the man who does not walk in the counsel of the wicked or stand in the way of sinners or sit in the seat of mockers." **Psalm 1:1**

"Listen to advice and accept instruction, and in the end you will be wise." **Proverbs 19:20**

"Do not make friends with a hot-tempered man, do not associate with one easily angered, or you may learn his ways and get yourself ensnared." **Proverbs 22:24-25**

"An unfriendly man pursues selfish ends; he defies all sound judgment." **Proverbs 18:1**

"A man of many companions may come to ruin, but there is a friend who sticks closer than a brother." **Proverbs 18:24**

not seen him at church on Sunday morning for over a month. He told me he was simply too tired because of the late Saturday nights. I observed that it seemed his friends were doing a better job of influencing *him!* Few things can have any greater impact on your character than the friends you keep. One of the best gauges of your values can be your friends.

Notice the biblical wisdom concerning friends in the Scripture to the left. Now write the main truth of each verse in your own words on a separate sheet of paper.

I encourage you to seek out friends who hold godly values, who are not timid about challenging you if you begin to stray from God's will. I have found that when I am with people who sincerely love the Lord, I also grow to love God more. When I am around people who desire to live holy lives, I am challenged to strive to make my life holy as well.

Are your friends drawing you closer to God and His will for your life? Use the following scale to rate the influence your friends are having on you. Check all that apply.

My friends:
❏ encourage me to walk closely with God
❏ lead balanced lives
❏ encourage my Scripture memory
❏ tempt me to compromise my beliefs
❏ pray for me regularly
❏ model Christlike behavior

❏ encourage me to be in church
❏ care enough to confront me
❏ live uncompromising Christian lives
❏ are critical
❏ are unreliable
❏ take far more than they give
❏ lose their temper with me

How do your friends rate? Remember, your friends will generally reflect your values. What is God saying to you about your current relationships?

Habits Change Hearts
Once you recognize you have values that impact your behavior, and you pick friends that affect your choices, a third area that influences your heart is your habits. Some habits are good and are known as disciplines. These may be study habits, exercise regimes, or regular church attendance. Other habits are bad and may be called addictions. These may include overeating, excessive attention to making money, or drug dependency. By observing my habitual behavior, you could soon determine what is most important in my life. You can alter your own character by allowing Jesus, through the Holy Spirit, to build healthy habits. For example controlling your anger, through the power of God, will eventually carve a niche of tenderness in your heart that will endure. After a while you will respond calmly without having to work at it.

Character determines the course of your life. Good habits build a noble heart. Therefore, guard your heart. *Using the verses on the next page as your guide, list some habits that will establish a healthy heart.*

How critical it is to guard your heart. When hearts are left unguarded Christians face their greatest defeats. Don't let this happen to you. What are some habits you could build into your life that would protect your heart? Check the following habits you practice.

- ❏ daily quiet time
- ❏ regular prayer group
- ❏ fasting
- ❏ watching Christian videos
- ❏ prayer partner
- ❏ regular church participation
- ❏ regular Bible study
- ❏ Scripture memory
- ❏ attending Christian conferences
- ❏ listening to Christian music

On a separate page, list five activities on which you spend your free time in a given week. Prioritize them in order of the most time spent to the least. Exclude mandatory activities such as sleeping, eating, attending classes, and work time.

• After evaluating the use of your time, what adjustments do you think God wants to make?

_____

• What is God saying to you about your habits?

_____

• What did God say to you during your study today?

_____

What will you do as a result?

_____

LESSON 4
Our Faithfulness: A Little Leads to a Lot

When I first met Gerry he was a university dropout who was in search of meaning and purpose. Gerry had a number of areas in his life in which he needed Christ to give him victory. I baptized him and became his pastor. I began to see God do a marvelous work in Gerry's life. He faced a crisis almost immediately after his baptism because his girlfriend ended their long-term relationship. In spite of his emotional turmoil, Gerry continued to seek the Lord's will for his life. About that time I received a call from a native Indian church; the pastor needed someone to come and help him with the work. We had a number of young people in our church who had expressed a desire to serve in some form of Christian ministry, but it was Gerry who volunteered to drive 200 miles each week in a vehicle held together by baling wire and hockey tape! When the native pastor resigned, the church called 24 year-old Gerry to be their pastor.

Five years later, Gerry felt called to go to seminary. He moved, with his wife and two toddlers, back to the city and earned his university degree. During that time he was asked to begin a new church in the city; so, while attending university and providing for his family, he pastored a mission church. When that church called a full-time pastor, Gerry was invited to spend his summer starting another church in a small town several hours away. That fall Gerry and his family packed their meager belongings and traveled 1500 miles to the nearest seminary to prepare for ministry. During his second year

"Rejoice in the Lord always. I will say it again: Rejoice! Let your gentleness be evident to all. The Lord is near. Do not be anxious about anything, but in everything, by prayer and petition, with thanksgiving, present your requests to God. And the peace of God, which transcends all understanding, will guard your hearts and your minds in Christ Jesus. Finally, brothers, whatever is true, whatever is noble, whatever is right, whatever is pure, whatever is lovely, whatever is admirable—if anything is excellent or praiseworthy— think about such things. Whatever you have learned or received or heard from me, or seen in me—put it into practice. And the God of peace will be with you."
Philippians 4:4-9

he was called as pastor of a small church two hours away. He moved to be near the church. This meant he had to arise at 5 a.m. in order to commute to his seminary classes two days a week. After three years of hard work in a challenging church, Gerry graduated from seminary and was invited to go as a missionary to Quebec, Canada. Quebec is one of the most unevangelized regions in the world today. For the next four years Gerry worked faithfully in that difficult mission field. Then, he received a call from the Canadian Convention of Southern Baptists to come and direct language work across Canada.

Today, Gerry bears only a faint resemblance to the scruffy university student he once was. As you might imagine, God has developed him into one of His effective servants. What made the difference in Gerry's life? His faithfulness. Gerry was always faithful in a little and God was correspondingly faithful to entrust him with more.

Question:
• What was the criterion for Gerry being entrusted with more responsibility?

_____

Faithfulness is a character trait that is highly praised by God. A student might not have many talents to offer God or many skills to put into His service, but he can be faithful. Jesus indicated that in the time of judgment it will be a person's faithfulness that will be praised. *Read what He said in the Scripture to the left.*

Questions:
• What was the basis of the master's praise of his servant?

_____

• What effect did the servant's faithfulness have on his master?

_____

"His master replied, 'Well done, good and faithful servant! You have been faithful with a few things; I will put you in charge of many things. Come and share your master's happiness!'"
Matthew 25:21

Jesus' standard for rewarding His children with greater knowledge of God or more responsibility from God rests on the level of trustworthiness in which they handle small responsibilities God has already given. If you can be faithful in the little things, He will trust you with greater things. If you do not treat each date with integrity, then God may be reluctant to give you a permanent marriage partner. If you are faithful in using the little money you have wisely, He may bless you with more. If you treat each friendship God gives you with care, He will expand your circle of friends.

God is consistent in the way He relates to people. For example, someone may decide to enter seminary and train to be a pastor after being a Christian only a few months. However God may say, "First join a regular Bible study at your church and learn some fundamental truths from My Word and then, when you have faithfully obeyed My Word in *your* life, I will prepare you to be an encouragement to others." God knows that your character and walk with Him may not be strong enough to handle any more responsibility than you presently have. If God has given you a small assignment, don't be discouraged but recognize it as a time of testing to see if you are prepared for a larger one.

Question:

• What might you conclude if God never gave you a larger assignment than what you already have? _____

A Frustrated Student

There was a college student in my church who was constantly in financial distress. She was not able to hang on to a summer job for long. She indicated that she always had difficult, unsympathetic bosses. Finally someone pointed out that it might not be her boss that had the problem. Rather, her poor job skills and her lax work ethic may have been the real culprits for her unemployment blues. It had not dawned on her that because she had not been trustworthy in her work, God was not honoring her with anything better. Take the following simple exam. Be as honest as you can.

FAITHFULNESS EXAM!

• How faithful have you been with God's Word? Do you study it regularly and obey it consistently?
❑ Yes   ❑ No

• How faithful are you in prayer? Do you pray regularly?   ❑ Yes   ❑ No

• How faithful are you with God's people? Are you an active member of a local church? Do you participate in the weekly activities of your church?
❑ Yes   ❑ No

• How faithful are you at being on mission with God? Are you always watching to see where He is at work? Are you presently involved in ministry with Him?
❑ Yes   ❑ No

• Are you a faithful witness? Do you regularly share your beliefs with those God brings across your path?   ❑ Yes   ❑ No

• Are you faithful with your finances? Do you spend your money wisely? Do you invest it in God's kingdom or only on yourself?   ❑ Yes   ❑ No

• Are you faithful with your college education? Do you strive to do your best and to be diligent in your studies?   ❑ Yes   ❑ No

• Are you a faithful friend? Are you the kind of person people desire to have as a friend?   ❑ Yes   ❑ No

• Have you been faithful with the family heritage God may have given you? Do you uphold the integrity of the Christian name that may have been passed on to you?   ❑ Yes   ❑ No

• Have you been a careful caretaker of the body God has given you?   ❑ Yes   ❑ No

• Has your Christian college group found you to be reliable in all they have asked you to do?

❑ Yes   ❑ No

• What did God say to you during your study today?

_____

_____

• What will you do as a result?

_____

LESSON 5
Our Failure: The God of Second Chances

Many times I have sat with an individual or couple as they wept and shared how they had forfeited God's best for their lives. It might be two college students confessing their moral impurity; or a student who had not been diligent in his studies only to be rejected by the school to which he had applied; or a student in bondage to addictive behaviors. The painful question is always eventually asked: "Have I blown it? Does God give a second chance? Could God use someone like me?"

Take your Bible and read Romans 8:28, 35-39.

Questions:
• According to these verses, what can separate you from the love of God?

_____

• Can failure separate you from the love of God? _____

• Is there anything in your life that God cannot work for good? How much is included in "all things" in verse 28?

_____

Scripture is clear. NOTHING can separate you from the love of God. Even your worst failure is no obstacle to the love of God. That does not mean you will not face inevitable consequences or God's discipline. It does mean that God will continue to love you and seek to bring about His best in your life despite whatever setbacks come from your failures. God's *assignment* may change but His *love* for you was forever settled on the cross and it will never change.

Questions:
• Have you experienced failure in your Christian life? In the space to the left, describe one area where you feel you have failed.

The wonderful thing about the Bible is that it is candid about the failures of men and women. If you ever think Christians are perfect, just read the Bible!

David the Murderer
There is probably no one in the Bible who had a more intimate relationship with God than David. Yet David committed some of the most despicable sins recorded in Scripture. When David should have been leading his army, he chose to allow his servant Joab to take his place (2 Samuel 11:1). While idling away his time David committed adultery with Bathsheba. If that were not a grievous enough sin, David subsequently had Bathsheba's husband Uriah murdered so he could marry her. What a horrendous resume of moral and spiritual failure: shunning his responsibility, theft, adultery, deception, and murder!

The prophet Nathan's scathing condemnation was earthshattering to David as he heard his sins denounced by the man of God (2 Samuel 12:7). Throughout Psalm 51 (read this carefully) you see the absolute brokenness and contrition David felt over his sin. Despite David's genuine repentance, God allowed some severe consequences of his sins which he endured the rest of his life (2 Samuel 12:10-14). Nevertheless, God forgave David's sin and loved and blessed him in many ways.

In his concern that he would never again be willing to sin against God in that way, David prayed. *Read his prayer in the Scripture to the right.*

Peter the Denier

Peter boasted of his courage and loyalty to Christ (Matthew 26:33). Yet before the night was over he would commit the classic failure of all recorded history! Peter began by falling asleep, in spite of Jesus' repeated pleas for him to pray with Him (Matthew 26:36-46). Later, while Peter was following Jesus from a distance, a servant girl recognized him. When asked if he was a follower of Jesus, he denied it. In all, Peter publicly denied he knew Jesus three times, the last time with a curse!

Luke described the result of Peter's failure. Take your Bible and read Luke 22:60-62. How devastating that look from Jesus must have been! How deeply ashamed Peter must have felt. Yet Jesus forgave him. Notice how gently and completely Jesus restored Peter (John 21:15-17). God would later allow Peter to preach the first sermon after Pentecost which resulted in 3,000 people being added to the church (Acts 2:41). Peter's second sermon brought another 2,000 men to the church (Acts 4:4). God used Peter in incredible ways, completely forgiving and overcoming his earlier failure.

Thomas the Doubter

The disciple Thomas had not been present when the risen Christ had appeared to the other disciples (John 20:24). The fact that all the other disciples were there may indicate that it had been a meeting that Thomas had chosen to miss. When he heard the animated reports from the disciples who had seen Jesus, Thomas responded with obvious doubt: *"So the other disciples told him, 'We have seen the Lord!' But he said to them, 'Unless I see the nail marks in his hands and put my finger where the nails were, and put my hand into his side, I will not believe it'"* (John 20:25). Even when all the other disciples believed Jesus and were excited about His presence, Thomas remained steadfast in his lack of faith.

Then Jesus appeared. He approached Thomas and showed him His hands and side. He saw the scars where Jesus had shed His blood for him, and Thomas could only respond: *"My Lord and my God!" (John 20:28).* Jesus restored Thomas to a place of faith in Him, and we never hear of him doubting Jesus again.

Our failures never catch Jesus by surprise. He is always prepared to respond to them. His love is never so overwhelmed by your failure that it does not continue to reach out to you. How should you respond to God when you fail? You might begin by claiming the verses to the right.

Questions:
• What must you do for God to respond to your questions?

"Search me, O God, and know my heart; test me and know my anxious thoughts. See if there is any offensive way in me, and lead me in the way everlasting."
Psalm 139:23-24

"'Call to me and I will answer you and tell you great and unsearchable things you do not know.'"
Jeremiah 33:3

"If we confess our sins, he is faithful and just and will forgive us our sins and purify us from all unrighteousness."
1 John 1:9

• What must you do to have your sins forgiven?

_____

• Do you think this means God will forgive ALL your sins?

_____

• How did God respond to the failures of David, Peter, and Thomas?

_____

• How will God respond to your failures?

_____

I have had the wonderful experience of seeing God take broken and sinful people and, by His grace, forgive and transform them into men and women of God. Only God could transform these lives! Perhaps you feel there are things about your life that will prevent God from ever using you for His kingdom. Remember, NOTHING can ever separate you from the love of God!

• What did God say to you during your study today?

_____

_____

• What will you do as a result?

_____

_____

INTRODUCTION

There was a fascinating episode on the original "Star Trek" television series entitled "Tomorrow Is Yesterday." In it, the crew of the U.S.S. Enterprise was accidentally thrown into a time warp and suddenly found themselves hovering above the United States during the 1960s. The United States Air Force immediately dispatched intercept aircraft to investigate. When the jet flown by Captain John Christopher began to break apart, the Enterprise "beamed" him aboard to save his life. Once aboard the starship, the amazed pilot was given a tour of the futuristic spaceship. To his dismay, however, Captain Kirk informed him that because he had seen the future, he could not be allowed to return to earth. If he were to return, Kirk explained, he could use his new knowledge and alter the course of history. Desperately trying to convince Captain Kirk that he should be sent home, Christopher countered by saying, "But then my disappearance would change something, too!" At this, Spock shook his head. "I have run a computer check on all historical tapes," he said. "They show no record of any relevant contribution by John Christopher."

Imagine being plucked from the earth and having to justify the value of your life to mankind before you were allowed to return. What evidence would you cite to prove your life made any difference?

LESSON 1
Developing Your Relationship

One of the most often-asked questions I hear from college students is: "How do I know if God is calling me to be a pastor? or a missionary? or a teacher? or a lawyer?" The problem is they are asking the wrong question. God does not necessarily call you to one, life-long job. He *does* call you to a relationship that lasts for eternity. God calls you to a *relationship*, then guides you to a *career*. Just as Jesus "called" John to "come, follow Me," so your calling as a Christian is to follow Jesus wherever He leads you. Your job is but an expression of God's current activity in your life. Your career may change several times throughout your life but your relationship with God is eternal. The jobs you hold will have no eternal significance in and of themselves but they are *vehicles* of God's eternal purposes when you are rightly relating to Him.

Read the following passages and indicate the places where God was working *in* Joseph and *through* Joseph:

MEMORY VERSE:

"Commit to the Lord whatever you do, and your plans will succeed."

Proverbs 16:3

THIS WEEK'S LESSONS:

Lesson 1
Developing Your Relationship

Lesson 2
Trusting God's Plan

Lesson 3
Hearing God's Voice

Lesson 4
Following God's Leading

Lesson 5
Investing Your Life

Career #1: Genesis 37:2: _____

Career #2: Genesis 39:1-2: _____

Career #3: Genesis 39:20-23: _____

Career #4: Genesis 41:39-45: _____

Questions:

• Which career do you think God wanted him to have? Why do you think God allowed Joseph to have so many different jobs?

_____

Joseph was originally a shepherd because that was the family business. He then became manager of a large household and excelled at his work. Next he was a prison administrator. Finally, he became the chief supervisor over an entire nation. That was quite a climb up the ladder! Which job did God want him to do? All of them. God led him to every position. Joseph's responsibility was to relate to God in obedience in *whatever* job he was assigned. As you walk with God, He may bring you through several jobs which provide different opportunities to serve Him and to grow in your relationship with Him.

Joseph trusted God implicitly so God used him in His eternal plan. It was critical for Joseph to hold a key position in the nation so God could use him to save thousands of Hebrews from starvation by bringing them to Egypt. Thus, God worked through Joseph and his career to build a holy nation for Himself.

Questions:

• As you prepare for a career, are you maintaining a close relationship with God? Is this affecting your career planning?

_____

• Has God begun to show you ways He might use you in a job to make a difference for His kingdom? Jot down what they are on a separate page.

• Are you willing to obey the next thing God tells you even if you cannot "see" all that God has in mind for your future? ❑ Yes ❑ No ❑ Almost

A Personal Example

People have asked me, "How did you know you were called to the job you are doing?" I have to answer that I have never felt called *primarily* to a job, rather I have always felt called to a relationship. During my days in university I held numerous jobs, even working on a fishing boat. My first "church job" was leading music and working with education programs. Later, that same congregation asked me to become their pastor. After this I became a director of missions for an association of churches and still later I was asked to work for our convention's Home Mission Board. Today I have a job that allows me to work for the Home and Foreign Mission Boards as well as the Sunday School Board. Which job did God want me to do? All of them! God was never as concerned with my particular job as He was that I walk with Him and listen to His voice.

Don't let yourself become so "hung up" with a particular job that you neglect your relationship with God. Each place of service is an opportunity for God to fulfill His purposes *through* you.

Career or Relationship?

While I served as a pastor I received a call from Bill, a church member. He worked with the government, made a good salary, and had plans for a comfortable retirement within five years. On this day, however, Bill had been informed that his position was being relocated to a town two hours away. God had given Bill a significant ministry in our church, and he knew he could not continue this work if he moved. Bill realized that refusing the transfer would mean forfeiting his job and losing the retirement income he had earned over many years. I clearly remember the service where he stood before the church to share his decision. He said he felt his relationship to Christ was more important to him than any job he might hold. He chose to forfeit his employment and trust God to provide for his needs, allowing him to continue serving in his church. The church prayed, and God DID provide another job within the same government which allowed him to retain his retirement. Bill continues to serve the Lord faithfully in his church today, and many people have come to know the Lord as a result. God does not always require us to make such dramatic choices, but He does insist that we place our relationship with Him above anything else in our lives and trust Him with our future. With HIM, our future is secure as God accomplishes His purposes through us.

Questions:

• Is your relationship with Christ more important to you than your career? Do you think you could give up any career if Christ asked you to for His sake? _____

• What did God say to you during your study today?

_____

• What will you do as a result?

_____

LESSON 2
Trusting God's Plan
Putting Your Faith on the Line

On June 30, 1859, over 25,000 curious spectators gathered along the edge of Niagara Falls staring incredulously at a tightrope stretched across the waterway, with no safety net below. Suddenly, a five-foot-five-inch acrobat by the name of Jean Francois Gravelet approached the rope. He called himself "The Great Blondin." He carried a 27-foot-long balancing pole as he stepped on to the tightrope. Despite several tense moments, Blondin managed to walk across the tightrope. He then began a series of death-defying stunts that left the audience spellbound. He carried a camera and tripod out to the middle of the rope to take a picture of the amazed crowd. He sat on a chair on the tightrope. He rode a bicycle; stood on his head; crossed while blindfolded, and pushed

Don't let yourself become so "hung up" with a particular job that you neglect your relationship with God. Each place of service is an opportunity for God to fulfill His purposes *through* you.

100
50
0

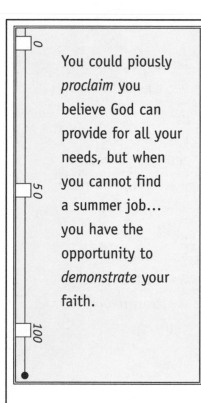

You could piously *proclaim* you believe God can provide for all your needs, but when you cannot find a summer job... you have the opportunity to *demonstrate* your faith.

"For I know the plans I have for you," declares the Lord, "plans to prosper you and not to harm you, plans to give you hope and a future." **Jeremiah 29:11**

a wheelbarrow across!

After these incredible stunts, he challenged the baffled crowd: "How many of you believe I could carry a man on my back across this tightrope?" After viewing his remarkable antics they readily acknowledged that Blondin was fully capable. Then came the unsettling question: "Which one of you wants to be that man?" Surprisingly, despite all their affirmations, no one was willing to risk his life. Blondin offered a substantial reward, but there were no takers.

Eventually, he enlisted a volunteer, Henry Colcord, to be his passenger. Colcord did indeed ride successfully on his back but only after being convinced of Blondin's reliability in the following way. Apparently, Blondin took Colcord to a room where a beam was placed six inches above the ground. Blondin stood on the beam and then challenged Colcord to push him off. Although Colcord pushed and pulled with all his might, Blondin's strength and balance were such that Colcord could not dislodge him. Colcord was finally convinced he could trust Blondin with his life.[1]

University students sometimes share the same mindset as the crowd watching Blondin. They are quick to agree that God is almighty and can do anything He desires. They will affirm that God can provide a job and meet their needs. But then God asks them to leave the safety of the shoreline and step onto the tightrope! THAT is where faith is put to the test. Your faith in God is not proven by what you SAY but by what you DO. You could piously *proclaim* you believe God can provide for all your needs, but when you cannot find a summer job, or you do not have enough money for rent or tuition, or your car breaks down, you have the opportunity to *demonstrate* your faith.

God Has a Plan

In this complex and fast-paced world it is easy to become discouraged about the prospect of finding a meaningful career. Technology is progressing so rapidly that in a matter of months one can become deficient in the latest skills and knowledge required for one's work. High unemployment rates make for stiff job competition. Companies are downsizing and laying off long-time employees, making job security a thing of the past. Of course, as bleak as the job market sometimes appears, God is perfectly capable of guiding your life so you are effective for Him in the workplace. A verse that often encourages university students is Jeremiah 29:11.

Questions:

• Do you believe God has a plan for your life? _____

• What do you sense God wants to do with your life?

_____

• Do you believe God can provide a job and opportunities to serve Him in the workplace? Why?

_____

• Have you firmly placed your future and career in God's hands? Will you?

_____

The people to whom Jeremiah 29:11 was written were in a hopeless situation. They were prisoners of the Babylonians, the international superpower of their day. They had no control over their education or job opportunities. From a human standpoint, the Israelites' future appeared bleak. Yet God said if they would trust Him and maintain their relationship with Him, they could be assured of His plans for their lives and have tremendous hope for the future. Just as God had a plan for the Israelites' future, He also has one for you.

Faith Pleases God

The challenge you face is whether or not you believe God and what He says about YOUR future. *In the Scripture to the right, notice what the writer of* Hebrews *says about your faith in God.*

Questions:

• According to the Scripture you just read, can you please God while struggling to believe Him? Explain.

_____

_____

"And without faith it is impossible to please God, because anyone who comes to him must believe that he exists and that he rewards those who earnestly seek him." **Hebrews 11:6**

• A lack of faith is more than a "weakness" or a "shortcoming." It is inherently displeasing to almighty God. God says in His word: *"everything that does not come from faith is sin" (Romans 14:23).* God WILL place you in situations where you will HAVE to trust Him. How will you respond when He does?

_____

A Student Who Obeyed

Peter was a college student in my church who strongly believed God was telling him to get involved in a student summer missions program. He was willing to go but faced the serious dilemma that he would have no money to enroll in school in the fall. *He understood what the Scripture said in the verse to the right.*

Nevertheless, he had already been denied a student loan, and if funds were not available in the fall, he would have to sit out a semester and find a job. He could not see the future, but he knew God could.

Peter chose to serve in summer missions. Upon his return, he faced a crisis in his belief in God because he did not have the money to enroll for the fall semester. I encouraged him to trust God and to watch how He would provide for him. On Wednesday evening Peter greeted me at church bubbling with excitement! Through miraculous circumstances, he had been granted a student loan which had earlier seemed unattainable. He had been offered a job that would perfectly fit his class schedule. Finally, a couple in the church had, under God's direction, invited him to live in their guest room, rent free! Peter had been obedient and God *was* faithful, providing everything that he needed.

If you never have to trust God, the people that watch your life will not see God at work and you will not have the opportunity to please God by your faith.

"And my God will meet all your needs according to his glorious riches in Christ Jesus." **Philippians 4:19**

Questions:

Check the following statements which apply to your life:

❏ Yes ❏ No I trust God to provide for all of my financial needs.

❏ Yes ❏ No I trust God to guide me into a career.

❏ Yes ❏ No I trust God with my health.

❏ Yes ❏ No I trust God with my future spouse.

❏ Yes ❏ No I trust God with my parents and family.

❏ Yes ❏ No I trust God with my school program.

• Has God put you in a circumstance where you are being forced to trust Him? If so, what is it? _____

• What have you been learning about trusting God lately?

_____

• What did God say to you during your study today?

_____

• What will you do as a result?

_____

LESSON 3
Hearing God's Voice

I sat one afternoon on a university campus talking with a young man who had a promising future. He was trying to decide whether to enter law school or enroll in a theological seminary to prepare for Christian service. Was one career more important than the other? Which one was God telling him to do? Which one was his own wishful thinking? One would involve remaining at the same school with his friends, the other would require him to relocate to a different state. These were all issues that were heavy on his mind as he sought to know for certain what God wanted him to do. I encouraged him that only as he related closely to God would he be able to hear God's voice and know what his next assignment was.

This kind of decision-making is not uncommon for university students. With just one life to live, decisions about where to spend your working life are critical. A wrong choice could lead to years of drudgery, wasting years toiling at jobs that seem to make little difference to the world around you. It is vital that you clearly know when God is speaking. You will only be able to hear His voice as you develop a *relationship* with Him.

A Fallacy

There is a heresy being taught today that God does not have a specific will for your life but is pleased to bless you as long as you do not sin. The Bible does not support this viewpoint. The moment you become a Christian, you accept the lordship of Jesus Christ, and *He* sets the agenda for your life. When a job offer or career opportunity comes along, there are at least four ways to determine God's will as revealed by His Holy Spirit. We will look at the first two during today's lesson.

1. The Holy Spirit speaks through the Bible.

Suppose you receive an attractive job offer. Friends and family may encourage you to take the job saying such things as: "Look at how much money you would be making! That's a respectable company. You would get to travel in that job. You would get your own office. The extra benefits would be great! You could get valuable experience with that company. This job would look great on your resume. It would be close to home!" In spite of the attractiveness of the prospective job, you would be wise to use the Bible as a guide to determine God's direction. The Holy Spirit will guide you through *biblical truths* as well as through *specific Scriptures*.

Biblical Truths

Look at the Scripture to the right and think of a truth that could be applied as you consider finding a job. I will complete the first one as an illustration.

I see at least five truths in these verses. *First, when the choice is between honoring God or obtaining a certain job, Scripture gives clear guidance as to what is most important.* I know people who refused high-paying jobs that would require them to compromise their integrity. In the competitive job market you face today, these pressures are sure to come and you will need to have built integrity firmly into your life.

A second truth is that it is good to work hard. I have had many people come to me and excitedly share about a job possibility that could make them well-off with only minimal effort on their part. I have cautioned them that when a job seems too good to be true, it probably is! Biblically, you are headed for trouble if your job choice is based on what will be the least demanding for you. Read Proverbs carefully and notice all it says about the consequences of laziness.

A third truth is that whatever job you have, you should commit it to the Lord. Could you wholeheartedly entrust the job you are considering to the Lord and would God be pleased with the work you would be doing? If you have committed your job to God, He will use it to bring glory to Himself.

Fourth, plan to be skilled in your work. Being a lackadaisical employee is despicable to God. Is the job you are considering one in which you are skilled or could become skilled? Is it a job in which you will strive to do your best? Never settle for mediocrity in anything you do.

Finally, money isn't everything! There is nothing wrong with earning a good salary. But the wage is rarely the most important factor in job choice. If you put all your effort into achieving higher paying jobs, you will "weary" yourself only to discover that the pleasures of this world are fleeting and do not provide the peace which comes only from a relationship with God.

Specific Scriptures

In addition to Biblical truths, the Holy Spirit will speak to you through certain Scriptures in order to give specific direction to your life. God will never contradict His word. That is, He will never tell you to do anything that is contrary to what He has said in

"The man of integrity walks securely, but he who takes crooked paths will be found out." **Proverbs 10:9**

Truth: As long as I am honest and refuse to compromise my beliefs at work, I know God will honor me and protect me on the job.

"Do you see a man skilled in his work? He will serve before kings; he will not serve before obscure men." **Proverbs 22:29**

"Do not wear yourself out to get rich; have the wisdom to show restraint. Cast but a glance at riches, and they are gone, for they will surely sprout wings and fly off to the sky like an eagle." **Proverbs 23:4-5**

Scripture. At times He will direct you to certain verses to guide you.

For example, you may be deliberating whether or not to take a job as a waitress. In many ways it is a good job, but it requires you to work on Sundays. As you are praying and asking God what you should do, you turn in your Bible for your daily Bible study and come to Hebrews 10:24-25. Read what these verses say.

Question:
• If this verse stands out as you read, what could God be saying?

_____

As you re-read these verses you sense that God is speaking to you. You remember the new Christians who are in the Bible study you lead Sunday mornings and realize that it is far more important for you to be at church and encourage fellow believers than it is for you to obtain this particular job.

Questions:
• Has God been indicating *through Scriptures* what kind of job He would like you to have? What has *He* been saying?

_____

2. The Holy Spirit speaks through prayer.

A second way the Holy Spirit will guide you is through your prayer times. If you regularly present to God every major decision you are facing, He will impress upon you what you should do. The Holy Spirit does this in several ways. If, each time you ask Him if you should take a certain job, God gives you a sense of divine peace, that will be one way God affirms your accepting the job. If, however, every time you pray you experience an uneasy spirit, it may be that God is cautioning you from proceeding further with that opportunity.

The Holy Spirit will also communicate with you by bringing Scriptures to your mind as you pray. For example, you might have the opportunity to work for a company that will treat you extremely well as an employee. However, the company may generate products that you know are immoral. You know you would have difficulty promoting the product, but you also reason that you might be a Christian witness in your workplace. *As you are praying about this decision, the Holy Spirit suddenly brings a passage of Scripture like the one to the left vividly to mind.*

Question:
• If you were suddenly reminded of this Scripture, what do you think the Holy Spirit might be saying about your job choice?

_____

You may feel that your own values and beliefs would not be adversely affected by your new work environment. You may even see how you could witness to others at work. Nevertheless, the Holy Spirit could be saying your employment for that particular company may have such a negative impact on others that it would do far more harm

"Therefore, if what I eat causes my brother to fall into sin, I will never eat meat again, so that I will not cause him to fall."
1 Corinthians 8:13

than good for your Christian witness. The Spirit knows all the consequences for others of your decision and may be cautioning you to consider more than your own needs in choosing a job.

Questions:
• Are you listening for God to speak when you pray? _____

• What has God been saying to you in your prayer times about the kind of work He wants you to do?

_____

• What did God say to you during your study today?

_____

• What will you do as a result?

_____

Circumstances alone can be confusing and must always be evaluated in light of what the Spirit also says to you through the Bible, prayer, and the church.

LESSON 4
Following God's Leading
Following Jesus to Toronto

Byron was a student of architecture in my church who sincerely wanted to follow Jesus. Jesus led him to Toronto, Canada's largest city and a place with a desperate need for the gospel. Byron found a job in a large architectural firm with excellent opportunities to use his training and talents. The more Byron became involved in God's work in that great city, however, the more he felt restricted by his company. God led him to quit his job and go into business for himself. Although this initially meant financial hardship and insecurity, it freed him to be an instrument of God in the metropolitan mission field. Today he is involved in starting a church which reaches out to the business people who work in the downtown core of that immense city, and God is blessing both him and his work. Like Byron, God will guide you to invest your life in His eternal work.

Yesterday's lesson dealt with two ways God speaks to you through the Holy Spirit. Write them from memory in the space at the right.

3. The Holy Spirit speaks through circumstances.

There is a third way the Holy Spirit will guide you in your job search. This is through your circumstances. Circumstances alone can be confusing and must *always* be evaluated in light of what the Spirit also says to you through the Bible, prayer, and the church. However, circumstances can help point you to God's will for your life.

Spiritual Markers

Circumstances can guide you if you pay attention to your spiritual markers. That is, those key times in your life when you know God has clearly spoken and has guided you. Take your Bible and read Joshua 4:1-7.

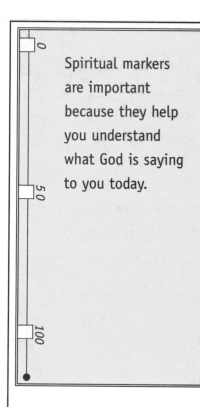

Spiritual markers are important because they help you understand what God is saying to you today.

Questions:
• In the Scripture you read, what did God want the people to do? Why?

_____

The children of Israel had just witnessed a miracle. God, by His divine power, had parted the Jordan River and allowed them to cross on dry land. God had dramatically reminded His people that He was on their side and, if they would obey Him, He would give them victory. Since people tend to forget even the greatest acts of God, He commanded the Israelites to build a stone monument that would stand as a permanent reminder of His power.

You may have instances in your life when God clearly indicates His will. God spoke to you at your moment of salvation. God spoke to you as a child, as a teenager, and during key moments in your life. Although God is present to speak to you during your quiet times, there are points at which God's word will be extremely clear to you. During these moments, it is important that you build a spiritual "pile of stones." I call these "spiritual markers." There are different ways to build spiritual markers. You can write what God said to you in a journal or write a note in your Bible (include the date). You may save special cards you received in the mail which God used to speak to you or pictures of key events in your spiritual pilgrimage.

Spiritual markers are important because they help you understand what God is saying to you today. For example, Mike became a Christian at an early age. As a child, he attended a summer camp where God clearly spoke to him about missions. When Mike was a teenager, God used a sermon by a visiting missionary to affirm His calling to pursue foreign missions. When Mike reached university, God spoke powerfully to him during one of his quiet times and again sensitized his heart to world missions. Then, as he approached graduation, a friend invited Mike to join him in his business. This would require a commitment of several years, but the job would be extremely lucrative. Mike asked God what he should do. As he looked at his spiritual journal, he noticed that from the earliest time he heard God's voice, God had consistently guided him in the same direction: towards missions. As Mike plotted out what God had clearly said, he saw how contrary this career opportunity would be to all God had told him to that point. His spiritual markers helped to clarify God's will.

Questions:
• Have you noted the spiritual markers in your life? What are some things you know God said to you:

     as a teenager _____

     as a university student _____

• If you have not already done so, record these in your journal or Bible. What pattern have you noticed in the things God has been saying to you?

_____

_____

• How do your current career plans match what God has said to you previously?

_____

_____

Open Doors Can Be Confusing!

Few things are more confusing to people than "open doors." An "open door" can be defined as any opportunity that presents itself to you. This can be a job offer, a proposal of marriage, or a major purchase. Many Christians assume that if God allows an opportunity to come, then it MUST be His will!

Read 2 Kings 20:12-18 and see the "open door" King Hezekiah entered.

Questions:

• What was the "open door" King Hezekiah faced?

_____

• In what ways did it appear attractive to "enter"?

_____

_____

• What was wrong with this opportunity?

_____

• What was the consequence of entering this "open door"?

_____

King Hezekiah jumped at the chance to "show off" to messengers of another country. Kings are always seeking alliances, and these messengers had come to him as friends. The problem was that in his eagerness to seize the opportunity, he sowed the seeds of Jerusalem's eventual destruction. These supposed "friends" reported all they saw to their king, and as a result, the king of Babylon eventually plundered Jerusalem.

"Closed doors" can be just as misleading as open ones. At times a door can appear to be "closed," that is, although you sense God wants you to do something, it seems impossible. Notice an apparent "closed door" that occurred as the children of Israel fled from the powerful Egyptian army. Behind them was a fierce enemy; in front of them lay an impassable sea. Read Exodus 14:10-13, 21-22.

Questions:

• How did the "door" the Israelites were facing appear to be closed?

_____

• Was it really closed? _____

A Door Closed by God

Paul faced a door that *was* closed by God. Read this account in Acts 16:6-7.

Question:

• How were doors "closed" for Paul?

_____

Paul sincerely wanted to evangelize Asia. He saw the tremendous need and he was willing to go. He had good intentions and desired to serve the Lord. God, however, had other plans for Paul. He would give Paul a vision telling him to go to Greece. God has the right to prevent you from going in one direction if there is something else He would rather have you do.

Not every opportunity that comes your way is from God. You must be sensitive to what the Holy Spirit is saying to you THROUGH your circumstances. Events in your life are neutral. It is what the Spirit says to you THROUGH those events that is important. Be sure to evaluate every "open" or "closed" door in light of what God has also said to you through the Bible, prayer, and the people of God. Hearing God's voice in the midst of your activities, however, will depend on how closely you maintain your relationship with Him.

Questions:
• What has God been saying to you through your circumstances?

_____

• What open or closed doors have you been facing? How have you verified them with the Bible, prayer, and the people of God?

_____

4. The Holy Spirit speaks through the church.
Your involvement in the church will be discussed further in chapter six, but it is important to note here that as you seek God's guidance concerning your career, your church can be a valuable instrument the Spirit of God uses to guide you. *Notice what the Apostle Paul said about the church in the Scripture to the left.*

Question:
• Notice how closely Paul said each church member should relate to the other. How will this intimacy between members affect you as you seek a job?

_____

> "So that there should be no division in the body, but that its parts should have equal concern for each other. If one part suffers, every part suffers with it; if one part is honored, every part rejoices with it. Now you are the body of Christ, and each one of you is a part of it."
> **1 Corinthians 12:25-27**

Paul was saying that members of a church should be so intimately connected that it is impossible for one to suffer without everyone feeling the pain. No member can enjoy success without everyone feeling joy. With such closeness, it is not surprising that church members would also be involved in the important process of choosing a career.

George W. Truett was an aspiring young lawyer until the members of his church urged him to enter the ministry. They had observed his life and were certain that God had gifted him for the gospel ministry. Truett listened to their counsel and became one of the greatest Baptist pastors of the twentieth century.

Likewise, the people of your church will have watched your life and witnessed God's activity in it. When you share job or career opportunities with them, they will be able to pray with you while already knowing many of the spiritual markers of your life. As part of a church family, you will be among young couples, college students, senior adults, youth, children, mature Christians, and brand new converts. You will know those who have been successful in business and those who have not, those who have struggled with their obedience to God and those who are pillars of faith. You will have access to the prayer warriors of your church who can intercede for you as you make your decision. You will have access to your pastor and other spiritual leaders who can give wise counsel as you seek to determine what God is saying to you. Each will have a unique perspective and experiences in their own walk with God which can help put your decision in focus.

Questions:

• Are you actively involved in a local church? In what ways?

_____

• To the right, list some of the people in your church through whom God has spoken to you. List what God said through them.

• What did God say to you during your study today?

_____

• What will you do as a result?

_____

> "Closed doors" can be just as misleading as open ones. At times a door can appear to be "closed," that is, although you sense God wants you to do something, it seems impossible.

> 100
> 50
> 0

LESSON 5
Investing Your Life

On October 25, 1992, Thomas Alva Edison was awarded a baccalaureate degree from Thomas Edison State College. The unusual thing was not that a man of his brilliance had earned a degree, but that he had done so 61 years after his death! Reese Jenkins, a history professor at Rutgers University, led a group of scholars to put together portfolios demonstrating Edison's learning. Edison's degree was not based on classes he had attended, but on the contribution he had made to society through his expertise.

Edison's example suggests that the important thing is not the courses taken nor the degree earned, but the life lived. A university education is not the end but the beginning. The education you obtain is merely a tool God gives you so you can be more effective in His assignment for you. The question at the end of life will not be: "what degree did you earn?" But, "what did you DO with your education? What did you invest your life in?"

John and Judas

The disciples John and Judas had the same basic education from Jesus. Both were trained for their calling during the three and a half years spent under Jesus' teaching. The education made no apparent impact on Judas. He left "school" the same as he entered it and tragically wasted his life. After John's schooling, he was a changed man. He took the education he received and invested it in eternity. History was forever changed because of the investment John made.

Questions:

• Are you making career choices based upon how God might influence eternity through you? ❑ Yes ❑ No ❑ Trying to

• How do you think your training and career could affect the kingdom of God? Jot ideas down in the sidebar on the left.

The Cambridge Seven

In 1885 Britain's attention was seized by seven university graduates who appeared to many to be throwing their lives away. All seven young men came from wealthy families and had received the finest education. Several were famous athletes. For example, C.T. Studd was the captain of the Cambridge cricket team and considered to be one of the finest cricket players in Britain. All seven had every opportunity available to wealthy young men, but each one had dedicated himself to foreign mission service in China. They became known as the "Cambridge Seven" and captivated the interest of Britain by walking away from lives of wealth and high society to spend their lives toiling in humble conditions on the other side of the world.

Many of these men faced strenuous appeals to forget their enterprise and take their place in polite society. However, they chose to follow their calling. Montague Beauchamp worked in China as an evangelist and later as a chaplain in Egypt, Greece, and Russia. He was offered an enormous fortune if he would return to Britain, but he refused. William Cassels served in China until his death. Dixon Hoste spent his life in China and was interred by the Japanese during W.W.II. Arthur Pohill ministered in China for 43 years. Cecil Pohill labored in China and eventually Tibet. Stanley Smith spent his entire life ministering in China. C. T. Studd served nine years in China before illness forced him home. Upon his return to Britain, he gave away his entire fortune. He later spent six years in India and then 21 years in Africa where he eventually died. Due in large part to the testimony of these men in Britain and the United States, the Student Missionary Volunteer movement was formed and encouraged numerous people to go out around the world as missionaries. A biographer of these men concluded his account by saying, "Not one of the Seven, except possibly C. T. Studd, was a genius. Theirs is a story of ordinary men, and thus may be repeated."[2]

The inspirational thing about the Cambridge Seven is that they had everything that this world has to offer, but they chose to turn their backs on it in order to follow Jesus. As a result, only God knows how eternity will be different. Until the end of time people will read of their lives and be encouraged to follow their selfless example.

Notice the promise to the left that Jesus made to His disciples as they were evaluating the investment they were making with their lives.

Questions:

• What did Jesus suggest you might have to give up in order to follow Him?

_____

• Have you had to give up anything in order to obey Jesus? What has it been?

_____

"Peter said to him, 'We have left all we had to follow you!' 'I tell you the truth,' Jesus said to them, 'no one who has left home or wife or brothers or parents or children for the sake of the kingdom of God will fail to receive many times as much in this age and, in the age to come, eternal life.'"
Luke 18:28-30

• What does Jesus say the "return" of your investment will be?

_____

Jesus was not unsympathetic to the price some would have to pay in order to follow Him. He just knew that the cost of NOT following Him would be far greater, and the reward FOR following would greatly surpass any loss. Jesus pointed to important things in people's lives: "home, wife, brothers, or parents, or children." I have received somber phone calls from those who said they dearly wanted to come and labor with me in pioneer missions, but they could not bring themselves to leave their home state. One young lady of 18 was threatened by her father that he would kill her if she were baptized in our church! She trembled all through her baptism. Upon her return home, she was not harmed, but her suitcase was packed and waiting on the back porch. She had been forced to give up both her home and her parents. There will be some hard decisions to make when you consider whether to invest in the temporal or the eternal.

Placed by God

I spoke recently with a young university graduate who was questioning why God had placed him in his job. It was a good job in the computer field. His responsibility was to relate to the top executives of some of the most prestigious companies in America. He commented that he was not sure how his life was "making an impact for God." I immediately sensed that God was intentionally putting this young man beside some of the most influential men and women in America for a Christian witness.

Many times I have been impressed with how God had strategically placed people in positions that were exactly where He needed one of His servants to be in order to carry out His redemptive purposes. I have talked with computer experts who rejoiced to find that their skills were desperately needed to assist Christian ministries in their effectiveness. School teachers perceived they were strategically positioned to influence impressionable minds toward Christ. Lawyers found that God was introducing them to some of the most hopeless men and women in society, many of whom were open to the gospel. Agriculturists have realized their particular skills were urgently needed overseas by people who, once they were fed, were ready to hear the gospel. Engineers have seen that through short-term mission opportunities they could revolutionize entire towns and villages both physically and spiritually through the skill and knowledge they had obtained in university. Businessmen ascertained that through the material wealth God had blessed them with, they could support struggling mission churches and other Christian causes.

Questions:
• How might God use you in your career choices for His kingdom?

_____

• Are you taking God's purposes into account as you prepare yourself for your career? How?

_____

• Always look at career from the perspective of eternity. Beside the following occupations, list ways God might use these professions to build His kingdom.

nurse: _____

engineer: _____

lawyer: _____

businessman: _____

teacher: _____

God can do far more with your occupation than you could imagine. A pediatrician, for instance, has numerous opportunities to serve God. She could be an active member of her church. She could minister to parents and children in a Christian manner, demonstrating God's love. Her office could provide Christian literature and music in the waiting room. She might serve in short-term missions in a needy place or use her income to sponsor mission work across North America and the world. Likewise, your profession, placed in the hands of the Lord, could become a powerful instrument for the furthering of God's kingdom.

Doctors on Mission

We had a number of medical students in a church where I was pastor. Some of them used their internship time to serve overseas and later were active in their churches. One medical graduate teamed with three other young doctors to settle in another part of the country where there was a need not only for a medical practice but also a church. The four partners committed to become the nucleus of a new church and to give their finances to support a pastor.

Unfortunately, there are people who assume that unless they are training to serve as a pastor or a missionary they do not have to consider how God might use their lives and occupations for His service. EVERY occupation is a calling from God. You can settle for the mediocrity of getting the job done and living for the weekend, or you can ask God to consecrate your daily work and use you to make a significant difference in His kingdom.

In the space to the left, list the four ways God speaks to you.

Questions:

• What did God say to you during your study today?

_____

• What will you do as a result?

_____

[1]Pierre Berton, *My Country: The Remarkable Past* (Toronto: McClelland and Stewart, 1976): 272-285.
[2]John Pollock, *The Cambridge Seven* (London: Inter-Varsity Fellowship, 1955; reprint ed., 1966), 111.

№4 RELATIONSHIPS:
For Better or Worse

0   10   20   40   100

INTRODUCTION
He Gave His Life for His Friends

On July 27, 1991, Kevin Brundrett, Stephen West, and Richard Letung went skydiving outside Kitchenor, Ontario. As the trio began their descent, West's and Letung's tandem parachutes became entangled, causing them to flap uselessly in the wind while the two friends plummeted toward the ground. Brundrett maneuvered himself over to them and, rather than pulling his rip cord, vainly attempted to disentangle their parachutes. Brundrett was a photographer and had placed a camera in his helmet so the entire sequence of dramatic events was captured on film. The film shows Brundrett desperately trying to pull up on his two friends' snarled lines in order to slow their fatal descent. Brundrett's parachute was in perfect working order and he could have pulled his rip cord at any moment to break his fall. But he refused to abandon his friends. All three were killed on impact.[1]

Jesus said: *"Greater love has no one than this, that he lay down his life for his friends" (John 15:13).* This is Jesus' standard for relationships, whether it is with your spouse, or friend, or parent.

LESSON 1
Friendships

Jesus knew the value of friends. The home of Lazarus, Martha, and Mary was a favorite place for Him to visit (Luke 10:38-42; John 11:1-5; 12:1-3). His heavenly Father gave Him 12 disciples to be His companions (John 17:6-8). Of these, Peter, James, and John became His closest friends. They were with Him during several of the crucial moments in His life (Matthew 17:1-8, 26:36-46; Luke 8:49-56).

Questions:
• Do you have close friends? ❑ Yes   ❑ No

• Name three of your friends and think why they are special to you.

Jesus was concerned that believers learn how God intended for them to relate to one another. To this end, He gave a beautiful demonstration of genuine friendship.
    Take your Bible and read John 13:1-20.

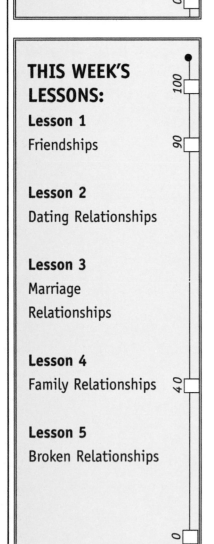

Questions:

• At what point in Jesus' life did He teach this lesson? Why was this time significant?

_____

• What lesson was Jesus trying to teach His disciples?

_____

• Why do you think Jesus concluded by saying: "whoever accept me accepts the one who sent me?"

_____

• How difficult would it have been for you to wash the disciples' feet?

_____

The timing of this event is important. It occurred during the Last Supper, the night Jesus would be arrested and condemned to crucifixion. Jesus knew He had little time left. Every word and action in His final hours was critical. At such a climactic moment, Jesus took a significant amount of time to teach them how they should treat each other. This lesson was highly practical. After walking a long distance in sandals on dusty roads, each disciple needed his feet washed. In their culture, feet were considered inherently unclean. So demeaning was it to wash someone's feet that Jewish slaves were not obligated to perform such a degrading task. Without a Gentile servant available, each disciple must have waited awkwardly, wondering what to do. Perhaps Jesus was looking to see if any of His disciples would serve the others. If so, He waited in vain. So, Jesus took the washbasin and towel and began washing each disciple's feet, including Judas, who would soon use those feet to run and betray Him. By performing such a menial task, Jesus was teaching that a friend is willing to put the needs of others before his own comfort.

Question:

• On a separate sheet of paper or at the end of the chapter, can you describe the last time *you* left your "comfort zone" in order to meet the need of a friend?

In John 13:20, Jesus taught the disciples a valuable truth. Christ resides by His Spirit in every Christian. When you meet a Christian, you encounter Christ. When you neglect or mistreat a fellow Christian, you are doing so to your Lord. This provides strong motivation for serving others! You are not to evaluate each person's worthiness or question if *they* should be serving *you*. It's irrelevant whether they can repay your kindness.

Cultivating Relationships

To my amazement I find that many Christians do not know how to be a friend. They are eager to receive but have no idea how to give. I talk with many college students who complain that they lack close friends. But the truth is, you have to *be* a friend to *have* a friend. I remember one student who complained to me that no one called on him socially. No one seemed to care whether or not he attended student events. He felt rejected and was considering dropping out of his Christian student organization. We examined his situation from another perspective: Who was he presently ministering to? Was he aware of students around him who were in difficult times? How many times had he called others and offered his services? He had not realized that the problem lay with him, and he determined to concentrate on *being* a friend.

Many people are ready to share *their* problems, but far fewer are willing to listen and take a genuine interest in *others* as Jesus did. As a Christian, you are without excuse for not knowing how to extend friendship. Jesus clearly demonstrated what a true friend is like. A friend looks for needs in others and then meets them to the best of his or her ability. A friend looks for Jesus' activity in the lives of others and then joins God in His work.

Qualities of a Christian Friend

These are the qualities Scripture says ought to be characteristic of a friend:

1. Faithful   Proverbs 17:17; 20:6
2. Honest   Proverbs 3:3-4
3. Good counselor   Proverbs 11:14; 12:15; 15:22; 19:20-21; 24:6; 27:9
4. Demonstrates spiritual fruit   Galatians 5:22-23
5. Wise   Proverbs 13:14, 20
6. Loving   Proverbs 17:17
7. Slow to anger   Proverbs 19:11; 22:24
8. Has integrity   Proverbs 10:9; 11:3; 11:30; 13:3; 20:7
9. Humble   Proverbs 22:4

Question:

• What kind of friend are you? Rate yourself on the following scale:

I give to others without expecting to receive.
❏ always   ❏ sometimes   ❏ never

I am too busy for friends.
❏ always   ❏ sometimes   ❏ never

I treat my friends as I would treat Christ.
❏ always   ❏ sometimes   ❏ never

I prefer being by myself.
❏ always   ❏ sometimes   ❏ never

I feel hurt if people do not minister to me.
❏ always   ❏ sometimes   ❏ never

I consider myself a good friend.
❏ always   ❏ sometimes   ❏ never

I watch for needs I can meet.
❏ always   ❏ sometimes   ❏ never

I am a reliable friend.
❏ always   ❏ sometimes   ❏ never

I find joy in helping my friends.
❏ always   ❏ sometimes   ❏ never

I am loyal.
❏ always   ❏ sometimes   ❏ never

I keep a 50-50 relationship with my friends.
❏ always   ❏ sometimes   ❏ never

How do you measure up as a friend? It is said that the way to tell if someone is a leader is by looking to see if anyone is following him. Likewise the way to tell if you are a good friend is to see if you *have* any friends. If you found that you didn't rate well as a friend, go back and read John 13. Ask God to help you become a friend to others as Christ was. Let Christ love others *His way* through you.

Iron Sharpens Iron

Read the wise advice Scripture gives about friendship in Proverbs 27:17.

Questions:
• According to Proverbs, what kind of influence should Christians have upon each other? How does this happen?

_____

_____

• Why do people need to be "sharpened"?

_____

Iron sharpens iron. Rub feathers or cotton puffs against a dull knife as hard as you want – the blade remains dull. It's the same with friends. There are those people who never challenge you to grow as a Christian. There are others, however, whose lives have a positive influence on you whenever you are around them. The book of Proverbs consistently urges you to surround yourself with friends who will bear a positive influence.

One of the benefits of close relationships is having people who love you enough to hold you accountable. The recent dirge of pastors, church leaders, and public figures who have fallen into moral failure has had one common denominator: they were accountable to no one. Many Christians today are taking Proverbs 27:17 seriously. They are finding two or three friends and forming an accountability group. These groups meet weekly and:

- memorize Scripture,
- tell each other what God said to them in their devotional times the week before,
- confess areas where they are struggling in obedience to God,
- hold each other accountable in these areas the following week,
- pray for each other,
- challenge each other where they notice "danger signals" for temptation.

Let me encourage you to find friends who want to be absolutely obedient to God and begin meeting with them regularly. It is best to limit the number of people involved so you feel free to share and get to know each other on an intimate level.

Questions:
• How does *your* love for others compare with the intensity of Jesus' love?

_____

• What kind of friend are you? What would you sacrifice for your friends?

_____

• *In the space to the right, list three things you intend to do in order to be a better friend.* Use Jesus as your model.

• What did God say to you during your study today?

_____

• What will you do as a result?

_____

_____

LESSON 2
Dating Relationships

A thirty-year-old pilot stealthily took off in his Cessna 150 airplane at 1:15 a.m. from the Edmonton municipal airport. He then "buzzed" the Londenderry neighborhood of Edmonton, Alberta for two hours, insisting upon speaking to his former girlfriend by radio. Finally, as his fuel ran out, with his estranged girlfriend still refusing to talk to him, he aimed his plane directly at her home and flew into the front window!

Extreme events like this demonstrate the terrible pain and confusion prevalent in many relationships between men and women. Divorce, family violence, and infidelity is rampant. In light of this, it is imperative that you seek God's leadership in finding a spouse.

The patterns you establish while dating will affect your marriage. Movies and television have lowered the standards and values in dating relationships to the base maxim of: "do what *feels* good!" You MUST allow God to establish the guidelines for your dating relationships if you are ever to have a dating life and marriage which pleases Him. What you do while dating reveals your *character* to God and to others.

The following four guidelines may help as you seek to maintain a dating relationship that honors God and the one you are dating.

1. Present your mind to Christ.

Christian dating too often reflects the *world's* thinking. Because you are a Christian does not mean you are doing "Christian" thinking! Notice what the Scripture to the right says.

Questions:
• What two desires can you set your mind on? What are the results?

_____

_____

"Those who live according to the sinful nature have their minds set on what that nature desires; but those who live in accordance with the Spirit have their minds set on what the Spirit desires. The mind of sinful man is death, but the mind controlled by the Spirit is life and peace."
Romans 8:5-6

Paul warned that concentrating on what the "sinful nature" desires will lead to death. Society spends billions of dollars encouraging people to satisfy their appetites. Pornography, Hollywood, even prime-time television all portray people as objects to satisfy your lust. If you fill your mind with pornography, soap operas, X-rated books and movies, this *will* affect your thinking about the opposite sex.

This is why Paul urged *"Finally, brothers, whatever is true, whatever is noble, whatever is right, whatever is pure, whatever is lovely, whatever is admirable—if anything is excellent or praiseworthy—think about such things" (Philippians 4:8).*

Apply this verse to your dating. Are your thoughts about the person you date noble? Admirable? Pure? Acceptable in God's sight? Think about these questions for a few moments right now.

> "Do you not know that your body is a temple of the Holy Spirit, who is in you, whom you have received from God? You are not your own." **1 Corinthians 6:19**

2. Present your body to Christ.

God created us male and female. He knew the joy and intimacy that was possible between man and woman in a marriage relationship. Read God's perspective on our bodies in the Scripture to the left.

I led a conference on a university campus where God began to convict many students concerning the way they had been relating to each other physically. Male students confessed to lust and pornography addiction. Women admitted they had been dressing to tempt and entice men. They realized that their actions were causing fellow students to fall into temptation. The students resolved to treat each other in a way that reflected that their bodies were the residence of the *Holy* Spirit. The way you treat your body reflects how seriously you consider God's habitation in you (Romans 12:1-2).

3. Present your conversation to Christ.

Read and observe what Jesus said to the religious hypocrites of His day in Matthew 12:34. These are strong words considering He was addressing a group of religious leaders. These pious men purported to be followers of God. In fact, their words were blasphemous! Jesus said that despite our best attempts to conceal it, what is in our heart will eventually come to light by what we say. Our true self will show through if we talk long enough. It's inevitable. This is certainly true on a date.

You may assume that because you are a Christian your conversation is always holy. Take a few minutes to reflect on the words that come out of *your* mouth.

While on a date, do you:
- ❏ usually talk about yourself?
- ❏ make fun of others?
- ❏ focus on the negative side of things?
- ❏ gossip?
- ❏ betray secrets?
- ❏ tell crude jokes and stories?
- ❏ criticize others?
- ❏ use profanity?

Questions:
• Are you pleased with what your conversation reveals about your heart?

_____

• How do you honor the person you are dating by your conversation?

_____

_____

• When you are on a date, do you feel comfortable discussing your relationship with God? _____

• Do the two of you pray together? Do you pray *for* one another? _____

4. Present your date to Christ.
Every time you go on a date, you have a four-fold responsibility. *You are responsible for the body God gave you; your Christian witness; the reputation of the person you are with; and the name of your family and church.* Relationships are a gift from God and are to be enjoyed. But, you should approach each one with a sense that there is much at stake.

In the Scripture to the right, notice how Paul said a husband should treat his wife.

Questions:
• What is it Christ did for His "bride," the church?

_____

• Should this apply to dating relationships? Why or why not?

_____

_____

You are to treat your love relationship the same way Christ loved the church. Christ saw people who were sinful and committed Himself to making them all that God desired. He cleansed the church through His redemptive work on the cross. Now He is preparing the church to be without stain, wrinkle, or blemish, but holy and blameless. This is a beautiful picture of a bridegroom who comes for his bride on their wedding day. Long before this, the bridegroom had lovingly helped his future bride to become all God intended, so now she would be holy and blameless. The careful stewardship of his bride's life allowed their marriage to begin untarnished.

Questions:
• Does Ephesians 5:25-27 accurately reflect the way you relate to those you date? Why or why not?

_____

5. Present your activities to Christ.
Dating activities are opportunities to develop friendships which, under God's direction, may lead to marriage. These activities hold potential for enjoyment as well as heartache. Take your Bible and read what Galatians 6:7-10 tells us.

"Husbands, love your wives, just as Christ loved the church and gave himself up for her to make her holy, cleansing her by the washing with water through the word, and to present her to himself as a radiant church, without stain or wrinkle or any other blemish, but holy and blameless."
Ephesians 5:25-27

Question:
• Do you see a truth in this Scripture? Write it in the space to the left.

God says you will harvest what you plant. If you nurture the spiritual life of the one you are dating and if you act with integrity, then you will enjoy the reward of a healthy relationship. If your dating relationship is based on honoring and serving God, you will have a solid foundation on which to build a marriage. Some of the college students in my church went on the most unusual dates! At times their "date" consisted of holding a worship service at the downtown rescue mission or a retirement home. Other couples took lonely senior citizens out with them on dates. Relationships were often built upon activities in the Christian student organization on campus. God blessed many of these couples, and they are still serving Him together today.

Other couples became ingrown, dropping their involvement in student organizations or church. They no longer made time to meet with other Christians. This was a recipe for disaster. God wants your relationships to be a blessing to others and not to be selfishly drawn inward. Couples who spend all their time with each other, not making themselves accountable to other Christians, face a much greater chance of falling into sexual sin.

I've had college students come to me devastated because they had been sexually active and now they felt unclean and ashamed. Nowhere does the Bible allow for sex outside of marriage. The word the Bible uses to describe sex between unmarried people is *fornication* (Ephesians 5:13; Colossians 3:5; 1 Thessalonians 4:3). It is always listed as a sin to be avoided. If you plant seeds of sexual sin while you are dating, you will harvest the consequences later: guilt, shame, and possibly an unwanted pregnancy. A relationship based on sex is a poor basis for marriage and will create numerous difficulties for the couple throughout their married life.

Paul offered hope to those facing this kind of temptation. *Read what he promised in the Scripture to the left.*

Questions:
• According to 1 Corinthians 10:13, are sexual temptations too powerful for you to bear? _____

• How does God deliver you from temptation?

_____

• How might this be applied to sexual temptation?

_____

Few temptations are as compelling as sexual sin. Even King David, the man after God's own heart, succumbed to it. Paul assures us that even this temptation is not powerful enough to overcome you. However, notice how God delivers you—He provides an opportunity to flee from the temptation. The best time for "escape" is not at the last minute. The moment the Holy Spirit *first* begins to alert you to danger is the time to flee!

"No temptation has seized you except what is common to man. And God is faithful; he will not let you be tempted beyond what you can bear. But when you are tempted, he will also provide a way out so that you can stand up under it."
1 Corinthians 10:13

• What did God say to you during your study today?

_____

_____

• What will you do as a result?

_____

_____

_____

LESSON 3
Marriage Relationships
A Wedding at Center Ice

Some people will do anything to ensure that their marriage gets off to a good start! Holly Holden and Roland Flaig were getting married in Winnipeg, Canada, and, like many young couples, they wanted their wedding day to be memorable. It was! The ceremony was held at center ice, between periods of a professional hockey game. The guest list included 12,500 fans, including the premier of the province. Flanking the wedding party was a large blue and white mascot named Benny and two radio personalities. Nevertheless, they would find that it is not the wedding, no matter how flashy, that determines the success of a marriage, but the biblical guidelines that are followed.

I have encountered marriages filled with great joy and fulfillment. Sadly, I have also known couples whose marriages held deep heartache. Marriage is one of God's greatest gifts. While in college, you will probably be considering and praying about marriage. You may already *be* married. Except for your relationship with Christ, no "invitation" from God holds deeper potential for fulfillment than marriage to the "right person" (Proverbs 31:10-31). At the same time, no relationship holds the possibility for deeper hurt than a poor marriage.

Today's study will look at God's pattern for marriage and choosing a life-partner. However, you may be doing this study from the background of: divorce; an abusive home; pressure from attitudes and values of the world around you; the "horror stories" of others; or just an honest fear of marriage. Don't allow the failures of others in marriage rob you of what God may have in store for you. If your parents did not model God's ideal for marriage, it is imperative that you seek guidance from God's Word and take your view of marriage from there.

Questions:
• Are there things about getting married that worry you? What are they?

_____

_____

The book of Hebrews says: *"Marriage should be honored by all"* (Hebrews 13:4). Marriage is a good thing, established by God at creation. *Notice what* Genesis *says about the first marriage in the Scripture to the right.*

> "The Lord God said, 'It is not good for the man to be alone. I will make a helper suitable for him.'"
> **Genesis 2:18**

Perhaps the greatest tragedy among students is when they refuse to trust that God will give them His best. Some panic and marry someone they know in their heart is not God's best for them.

Questions:
• Why did God establish marriage?

_____

• How is the wife described here in Genesis?

_____

God first established marriage for *companionship*. The word "helper" does not denote inferiority; it is the same word used in the Old Testament to describe God's relationship with His people. This verse describes the joining of two people so that they are made stronger together than when they were apart. The woman was "suitable" for the man, meaning that no other creature was adequate for the intimate level of relationship God desired for man. Together, husband and wife are able to help each other achieve all that God has planned for them.

Questions:
• Has there been divorce or marital strife in your home? If yes, how has this affected you? Will you allow God to help you forgive, "break the chain," and establish a Christ-centered home? How do you plan to do this?

_____

_____

_____

Falling in Love
The best prevention for divorce is to marry wisely. It is important to recognize you can "fall in love" with more than one person. God made each of us in His image (Genesis 1:26-28), and each has a God-given purpose. Therefore, many people hold the potential to become "special" to you. I have known college students who planned to marry someone with whom they were obviously incompatible. Yet when asked why they were getting married, they answered, "We are in love!" This sounds great, but feelings can be deceptive. The obvious question, then, is, "If 'being in love' is not enough to base my marriage on, what *do* I use as a standard?" God's Word holds the answer. Consider the following three guidelines:

1. Trust God's plan for your life.
Jeremiah 29:11 says: *"For I know the plans I have for you," declares the Lord, "plans to prosper you and not to harm you, plans to give you hope and a future."* Do you trust God's will for your marriage? Do you believe that God will give you only that which is an expression of His perfect love? This may mean His special assignment is for you to remain single; *that* could be His expression of love to you. If He wants you to marry later in life, this is what He will lead you to do. The important thing is that however He leads you, *that* is where you will find peace and joy, lacking nothing.

Perhaps the greatest tragedy among students is when they refuse to trust that God will give them His best. Some panic and marry someone they know in their heart is not God's best for them. As graduation approaches they may feel pressure to be married. Or they may become depressed if they pass the age at which they always thought they would marry. As more of their friends get married, they may determine to marry also. I have urged many students in these situations to trust that God's will is *always* best for them and to *never* take matters into their own hands. Waiting is sometimes the hardest form of obedience.

Single but Hopeful!

While I was a pastor I came to know a marvelous woman named Evelyn. For many years she had faithfully served the Lord as a missionary in India and then in Venezuela. When her mother became elderly, Evelyn returned home to care for her. She joined our church, taught in our Bible college, and befriended many of our college students. Evelyn had never married but had committed her life to God's perfect will. Smiling, she would often tease, "I'm single but still hopeful!" After her mother passed away, God introduced Evelyn to a widowed missionary and they were married. Today they enjoy a wonderful ministry sharing the Gospel with Sikhs in Canada.

Question:
• Are you ready to *completely* trust God regarding your marriage partner? (Psalm 84:11) If not, what is holding you back?

---

2. Cultivate your most important relationship.

Jesus said*: "But seek first his kingdom and his righteousness, and all these things will be given to you as well" (Matthew 6:33)*. He also instructed: *"Therefore do not worry about tomorrow. . ." (Matthew 6:34)*. Jesus said in *Matthew 6:8, "Your Father knows what you need before you ask him."* God promised that if you will always place Him first, He will provide for every need in your life. That includes marriage.

3. Determine to marry only a committed Christian.

Few biblical instructions, when ignored, have created more sorrow and pain than Paul's warning: *"Do not be yoked together with unbelievers. For what do righteousness and wickedness have in common? Or what fellowship can light have with darkness? What harmony is there between Christ and Belial [the devil]? What does a believer have in common with an unbeliever?" (2 Corinthians 6:14-15)*. The Bible is absolutely clear, Christians should *not* marry non-Christians. Paul said that Christians and non-Christians are fundamentally different. One is a servant of Christ, the other an enemy of Christ. One is light, the other darkness. One seeks to put Christ first in everything; the other lives for self. It is an impossible combination.

I have seen much heartache in Christians who married unbelievers. Their hopes as well as the promises of their unbelieving fiance(e), had never materialized. As a pastor I had several wonderful Christians who served faithfully in the church; however, they served alone. Their non-Christian partners rarely, if ever, attended church or supported their ministry. Often their spouse would ridicule their faith and refuse to cooperate in raising their children to honor God. One husband even killed his Christian wife in a fit of anger. These people suffered greatly from being yoked with an unbeliever and would often plead tearfully for the church to pray for their husband or wife. Their agony confirmed in my heart that the most effective way to avoid marrying an unbeliever is not to date them. Remember, you can develop "feelings" for people if you spend enough time with them. Be careful you do not spend too much time with those God forbids you to marry.

Samson's Example

Judges 14-16 tells the story of Samson, a young man for whom God had big plans. God blessed Samson with unusual strength. Yet Samson was attracted to a woman named Delilah. Delilah may have had physical beauty, but she did not revere God, or love Samson. By marrying the wrong person, Samson forfeited what God might have done with his life, to say nothing of his own happiness. This story stands as a poignant example of the dangers of marrying an unbeliever.

Notice the example of the couple in the Scripture to the left.

Questions:

• What characteristics do you notice about this couple?

_____

"In the time of Herod king of Judea there was a priest named Zechariah, who belonged to the priestly division of Abijah; his wife Elizabeth was also a descendant of Aaron. Both of them were upright in the sight of God, observing all the Lord's commandments and regulations blamelessly." **Luke 1:5-6**

Zacharias and Elizabeth were "upright in the sight of God." Can you imagine a marriage relationship in which God saw you and your spouse as "upright" and "blameless" in your obedience to Him? No wonder God gave them such an honor. Zacharias and Elizabeth were the parents of John the Baptist. These people were not extraordinary or superior in intellect. They were simply people who were deeply committed to God and united to obey His will for their family. What could God do through you and your family? Only He knows! Be absolutely faithful to Him and see what He unfolds for your life!

Optional Exercise

Set aside a special place in your spiritual journal; list the character traits God requires for those He uses and blesses. Include Scripture references. Begin praying each day that God would build these qualities into your life so that you would be the kind of person God would entrust with His "best."

• What did God say to you during your study today?

_____

_____

• What will you do as a result?

_____

_____

LESSON 4
Family Relationships

I had the privilege of being raised by Christian parents who prayed for me regularly and encouraged me to walk closely with God. Considering their influence, it is not surprising that I committed my life to Christ nor that I became a pastor. Several years ago, however, I made an interesting discovery. I was visiting England and Wales for the first time in order to see the home of my ancestors. I preached in a church in Wales and discovered that there had been four Blackabys who had preached there before me. I discovered that in the days when the famous Charles Haddon Spurgeon led his Bible College, three of my forefathers were there preparing themselves to be ministers. God spoke to me: "My work in your family did not begin with you or your parents. I have been working in your family for much longer than you know. Many of your relatives have faithfully served Me and now it's your turn." God assured me that much of the blessing I enjoyed was because of their faithfulness to God in their day.

Perhaps you have been blessed with a Christian grandmother who prayed for you; an uncle who was a missionary; parents who took you to church. If so, you now have a responsibility to "take the baton" and run your portion of the race well. Or maybe you are a first-generation Christian. You may not know another Christian in your extended family. God's invitation to you is to begin the Christian heritage in your family, and several generations from now your descendants will look to you as the originator of the good work God has done in your family.

A Heritage Honored

The Apostle Paul wrote to Timothy about his family heritage. *See what he said in the Scripture to the right.*

Questions:
• What is it Timothy received from his grandmother and mother?

_____

• What was Timothy to do to avoid taking this for granted?

_____

Timothy had a "sincere faith," which Paul recognized as a response to the example of his grandmother and mother. Because of their faithful witness and prayers Timothy developed his own faith. Paul urged Timothy not to take this Christian heritage for granted, but to build upon the faith that had been passed on to him.

A Heritage Dishonored

I read about a young man who became dissatisfied with his life. He came from a good home with parents who loved him. They gave him every opportunity for happiness and success and were, even then, grooming him for the family business. This young man, however, was restless. He felt stifled. Despite his parents' pleading, he took an early inheritance and traveled abroad. There he found some "fast-paced" friends, the kind who lived only for the next party. Because of his wealth, the young man became

> "I have been reminded of your sincere faith, which first lived in your grandmother Lois and in your mother Eunice and, I am persuaded, now lives in you also. For this reason I remind you to fan into flame the gift of God, which is in you through the laying on of my hands."
> **2 Timothy 1:5-6**

instantly popular. He gratified all of his desires and enjoyed himself. Life seemed better than ever. Then his money ran out, and so did his friends. He looked in vain for a job to support his lavish lifestyle. Driven at last by hunger, he was forced to take a demeaning job at starvation wages. In poverty and shame, his mind was flooded with fond memories of his home and the love he had experienced. He concluded that his home-life had to be better than what he was experiencing and he headed home.

As Jesus told this story in Luke 15:11-32, He said that when the prodigal son returned, his father was watching for him. When he saw his errant son in the distance he was filled with joy and, disregarding dignity or protocol, ran to meet him. Jesus told this story to illustrate the love and forgiveness that our Heavenly Father has for us and the joy He experiences when we return to Him.

This same pattern can occur in university. I have spoken with many college students who were raised in a Christian home. Then in college they are swept up into a blatantly amoral environment. Before long, many of the values, beliefs, and practices the student had been raised to affirm are discarded for the new lifestyle of "living for the moment." How often I have heard college students weep as they confessed they were "prodigal" sons or daughters who had rejected their Christian heritage, only to discover that what they received in return was emptiness and regret!

Questions:
• Are you honoring your heritage? How?

_____

_____

Take your Bible and read carefully the fifth commandment (Exodus 20:12).

Questions:
• What is God commanding you to do in Exodus 20:12? How do you do that?

_____

_____

• Was God's command for those with Christian parents only?

_____

The first commandment God gave concerning relationships was regarding parents. God says to "honor" them, showing them respect. Paul noted that this was the only commandment that carried a "promise" (Ephesians 6:2). The promise is that God will give you a full and meaningful life if you honor your parents. You may feel you cannot honor them because of abuse or neglect you experienced at their hands. This does not cancel the command of God, which He assures brings blessing.

How should you respond to parents who caused you pain or suffering or disappointment?

First, God tells you to forgive. Jesus taught His disciples to pray: *"Forgive us our debts,* *as we also have forgiven our debtors" (Matthew 6:12).* The reason to pray this way, said Jesus, is because *"If you forgive men when they sin against you, your heavenly Father will also forgive you. But if you do not forgive men their sins, your Father will not forgive your sins"* (Matthew 6:14-15).

Questions:

• According to the above passage, on what basis does God forgive your transgressions against Him?

_____

_____

• If you forgive your parents, does this mean you have not been hurt by them?

_____

• Is being deeply hurt by someone an acceptable excuse for not forgiving them? Why?

_____

_____

Second, you are to love them. No greater honor can you bestow on your parents than to love them as God loves you. How does God love you? Romans 5:8 says: *"But God demonstrates his own love for us in this: While we were still sinners, Christ died for us."*

Question:

• What were you like when God began loving you? Did you deserve His love?

_____

• What are some ways God has expressed His love to you?

_____

Third, be completely obedient to God's will. Ultimately there is no better way to honor your parents than by allowing God to work in and through your life to bring Him glory.

Fourth, live a life of holiness that influences others, including your family. Jesus said you were to be the "salt" and "light" of the world (Matthew 5:13-16). You may be the only Christian witness your family has. Because they know you so well, the most difficult people in all the world to witness to may be your family. However, your family will also notice the changes in you once you become a Christian. When God saved you, it was His invitation for you to join Him in His redemptive work for your family.

Like Ripples in a Pond

While I was a pastor, I baptized a fine university student named Karen. She was the only Christian in her family. Her father was a known alcoholic in her home town. Now

> You are to love your parents. No greater honor can you bestow on your parents than to love them as God loves you.

100

50

0

that she was a Christian, Karen had a new love and concern for him, and asked us to pray for him. It wasn't long before her father became a Christian, and he remains a strong Christian witness in his community today. Karen's friend Becky, from the same town, also became a Christian, and Becky's mother attended her baptism. So clear was Becky's testimony that her mother tearfully asked if she could speak with me after the service. She had been seeking God for 28 years. That night she put her faith in Christ and within a week invited us to lead a Bible study in her home 128 miles away. We did, and a church started there that began reaching out to the town and surrounding area.

Questions:

• What are specific ways you can be "salt" and "light" to your relatives?

_____

_____

_____

• What are challenges you face in witnessing to your relatives?

_____

_____

• What specific changes should you make in the way you relate to your family?

_____

_____

• *If there have been other Christians in your family, list them in the space to the left, and the influence they had upon you.*

• *If you are a first-generation Christian, list those you are praying for and witnessing to as you seek to begin a Christian heritage.*

Optional Exercise

Write a letter today thanking someone in your family for the Christian influence they had on you.

• What did God say to you during your study today?

_____

_____

• What will you do as a result?

_____

LESSON 5
Broken Relationships

As a student, I participated in a religious survey in the neighborhood surrounding my church. When I came to a house across the alley from the church, I was greeted by a weathered-looking, middle-aged woman. When I told her what I was doing, she said, "Oh, I used to go to that church. In fact I'm probably still on the membership roll." She went on to describe how 20 years earlier she and her family had attended the church. Then one day, someone in their Sunday School class made an off-hand remark that deeply offended them. They left the church and never returned. When I asked about her family, she gave me a pained look. Her oldest daughter was in prison, and her youngest daughter was in a drug rehabilitation center. Her husband had divorced her several years earlier. She told me that she watched some religious programming on television and that was all the "church" she had anymore.

As I walked away from her home that afternoon, I was heavy-hearted. Here was a woman who had allowed a broken relationship to keep her and her family out of the church for over 20 years. As she nursed her hurt feelings, her children grew to disregard the teachings of God for their lives. The mother stood alone and embittered with her family crumbling around her and never made the connection that her unwillingness to heed God's instruction on reconciliation had caused enormous heartache in her family. As her family was in shambles, she lived across the street from a group of Christians who could have supported her family through their times of crisis.

An unmended relationship can fester until it destroys all it touches. *God knows how devastating this can be, so He gives clear instructions for reconciliation in the Scripture to the right.*

Questions:

• What might you be doing when you realize you have a broken relationship?

_____

• What does Jesus say to do about the relationship?

_____

_____

• According to this passage, does it matter who is at fault?

_____

_____

> "Therefore, if you are offering your gift at the altar and there remember that your brother has something against you, leave your gift there in front of the altar. First go and be reconciled to your brother; then come and offer your gift."
> **Matthew 5:23-24**

The cost of NOT reconciling is always far greater than the cost of reconciling. Reconciliation is always worth it and always pleasing to God; it sets you free!

0

50

100

Jesus gave clear instructions for those suffering from broken relationships. The context of Jesus' example is this: you come to church and, in the course of your worship, realize there is someone who has something against you. In this example, it is the *other* person who is upset at *you*. It may be something you did which offended them or perhaps something they only perceive that you did. Regardless of the legitimacy of their concern, the directions are the same. Jesus said "go" and "be reconciled." That is, as a Christian, if you realize someone is angry with you, do not wait for *them* to come to *you*. Rather, always take the initiative and go to them. Interestingly, the command is NOT "try and be reconciled" or "do what you can and hope they get over it," but "BE reconciled!" That is, YOU take the responsibility to strive for reconciliation and do not give up until you HAVE been reconciled! A Christian should never be satisfied as long as he knows someone has "something" against him. A broken relationship affects your relationship with God and therefore, will cost *you* dearly, maybe for years.

Questions:
• Do you have any broken relationships right now? _____

• What has happened *in you* because of your broken relationship?

_____

_____

• What has happened to others?

_____

_____

It is important to see how God looks at broken relationships. He wants life's *best* for you. Some things rob you of God's best.

Christ Brings Reconciliation
Take your Bible and read Romans 5:6-10. Based on this Scripture:

Questions:
• What did Christ do for you?

_____

• Who paid the biggest price for your reconciliation, you or God?

_____

• How does reconciliation with God bring "life"?

_____

_____

God took the initiative to be reconciled with you. He committed no offense. He loved you, yet you were an "enemy" of His. God refused to accept the broken relationship. He did not wait for *you* to come to *Him*; God paid the price for reconciliation. You will find that often the offended person must pay the higher price to bring reconciliation. The cost of NOT reconciling is always far greater than the cost of reconciling. Reconciliation is always worth it and always pleasing to God; it sets you free!

Questions:
• Are there any broken relationships that are limiting God's activity *in* your life?

_____

• What are some serious consequences of your NOT being reconciled with others?

_____

_____

• What is preventing you from taking the initiative to be reconciled today?

_____

_____

God Gives the Strength

In her powerful book, *The Hiding Place*, Corrie Ten Boom told of when she first came face to face with a prison guard who had tormented her during her imprisonment in the Ravensbruck concentration camp during the latter days of World War II. As she recalled:

It was at a church service in Munich that I saw him, the former S.S. man who stood guard at the shower room door in the processing center at Ravensbruck. He was the first of our actual jailers that I had actually seen since that time. And suddenly it was all there—the roomful of mocking men, the heaps of clothing, Betsie's pain-blanched face. He came up to me as the church was emptying, beaming and bowing. "How grateful I am for your message, *Fraulein*. To think that, as you say, He has washed my sins away!" His hand was thrust out to take mine. And I, who had preached so often to the people in Bloemendaal the need to forgive, kept my hand at my side. Even as the angry, vengeful thoughts boiled through me, I saw the sin of them. Jesus Christ had died for this man; was I going to ask for more? Lord Jesus, I prayed, forgive me and help me to forgive him. I tried to smile, I struggled to raise my hand. I could not. I felt nothing, not the slightest spark of warmth or charity. And so again I breathed a silent prayer. Jesus, I cannot forgive him. Give me Your forgiveness. As I took his hand the most incredible thing happened. From my shoulder along my arm and through my hand a current seemed to pass from me to him, while into my heart sprang a love for this stranger that almost overwhelmed me. And so I discovered that it is not on our forgiveness any more than on our goodness that the world's healing hinges, but on His. When He tells us to love our enemies, He gives, along with the command, the love itself. [2]

Questions:

• How was Corrie able to forgive her former guard?

_____

_____

• Could this happen in your life?

_____

_____

• What did God say to you during your study today?

_____

_____

• What will you do as a result?

_____

_____

[1]*Winnipeg Free Press*, "Inquest told of 'heroic' bid to save pals," November 27, 1991, A5.
[2]The Hiding Place, 215.

Nº 5 CRISES:
Your Moments of Decision

0   10   20   40   •   100

INTRODUCTION

A Childhood Decision

I listened to an African-American singer capture the hearts of hundreds of people as he sang gospel songs at the World's Fair in Vancouver in 1987. Earnest was a happy man with a tremendous baritone voice. He told me his story. He grew up "on the wrong side of the tracks" in Alabama. One day, in the midst of poverty and hardship, he heard a gospel singer on television. He prayed, "Lord, if you help me to sing, I'll give You my voice to serve You!" He began winning first place in music contests at school. He majored in voice at university. At his graduation recital, a Christian opera singer from the Metropolitan Opera in New York City approached him and asked, "Would you audition for the opera? You are *certain* to make it!" Earnest went out on a hill overlooking the city in order to think and pray. There God reminded him, "Earnest, as a boy of five years old, you asked Me to help you sing. You said if I did you would give ME your voice. I've done My part. Will you do yours?" Earnest was filled with emotion as he remembered his vow to God. He bowed his head and gave his life to God to sing gospel music wherever God asked. In the midst of hardship, he had decided to put his life entirely into God's hands. He has never gone back on his word and on the day I heard him, he was moving hundreds to tears as he sang for God at the World's Fair in Canada.

A crisis is a challenge but also an opportunity for the Christian. We are tempted during crises to surrender to the world's viewpoint. During such difficult times we endure the loss of friends, ambitions, or possessions and are often discouraged. From a human perspective crisis means loss. But God plans that we benefit from every trial we face. Examine some benefits of facing a crisis.

LESSON 1
Crises Point to God's Unwavering Love

God's Character

Once you reach college age you will face some life-changing choices. As an adult, there is far more at stake in your decisions than as a child. Now is the time to prepare yourself for the crises that are certain to come. Many people immediately *blame* God for every hardship in their lives. They may ask, "Why did God do this to me? If God is so

MEMORY VERSE:

"And we know that in all things God works for the good of those who love him, who have been called according to his purpose."

Romans 8:28

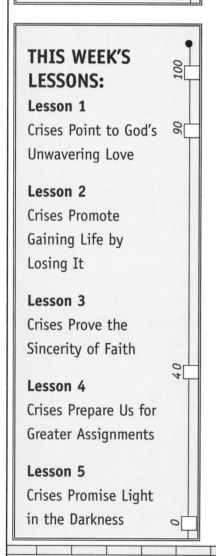

powerful, why didn't He prevent this tragedy?" The way you respond to a crisis can dramatically affect the rest of your life. What you do in times of distress *reveals* what you believe about God. Unless you clearly understand God's nature, you will never be able to properly respond in times of trial.

Read the Scriptures at the top of the next page and note what God is like. Based on these Scriptures:

Questions:
• What one word describes the nature of God?

_____

• How does God demonstrate His love for you?

_____

God's Love in the Midst of Crisis

Richard and Lisa were married the summer after they graduated from university and then traveled 1,500 miles to attend seminary. Richard sensed God leading him to be a pastor and knew God wanted him to earn a seminary education. As he neared the completion of his Master of Divinity degree, Richard knew God was inviting him to enter the Ph.D. program. They had already spent three years at seminary and were eager to serve in a church in Canada. Yet they were obedient to God's instructions to stay and Richard began doctoral studies that fall.

During the first semester of the Ph.D. program, a deluge of crises almost overwhelmed them. Lisa's father suffered a massive heart attack and clung to life for three weeks before dying. In addition to their grief, Richard and Lisa faced financial hardship from work missed, and Richard was far behind in the demanding Ph.D. program. One month later, Lisa's mother was diagnosed with cancer, a disease that would soon take her life. The following month, bad news came again, this time concerning Richard's 16-year-old sister Carrie. She, too, had been diagnosed with cancer and would undergo extensive chemotherapy treatments.

In that fall semester they were hit by one tragedy after another. They had been obedient to God. Why was He allowing this to happen? In the following months, God did an amazing work in their lives. He made His love, presence, and peace known to them in a deeper way than they had ever experienced before. Later, as pastor and wife, they encouraged many others who were suffering in similar ways. After some years, Richard was called as president of the Canadian Southern Baptist Seminary. During the first semester, Lisa was asked to speak to the wives of the seminary students. She told them of her own pilgrimage as a student's wife and of the difficulties she had experienced. She shared how the grace of God had sustained her. Many of the women were deeply moved and said, "It means so much to us that you know what we are going through!" In that moment, God affirmed, once more, why He had allowed them to endure such suffering. Not only did God want them to experience His peace and comfort but He was also preparing them to minister to seminary students, many of whom would undergo similar difficulties. God took their loss and brought good from it. He is always able to do that.

Questions:

• Have you ever tried to be obedient to God, only to face hardships? What happened?

_____

• What "good" did God bring out of the challenges you faced? Did you allow God the time to bring it about?

_____

_____

• Do you feel that because you are a Christian, you should not have to face hardships? Why or why not?

_____

_____

> "This is how we know what love is: Jesus Christ laid down his life for us."
> **1 John 3:16a**

> "And so we know and rely on the love God has for us. God is love. Whoever lives in love lives in God, and God in him." **1 John 4:16**

God's nature is perfect love. God would have to go against His nature to give you less than His best. Settle this point decisively in your mind. God perfectly revealed His love when Jesus died on the cross for your sin even while you were His enemy (John 3:16; Romans 5:5-11). If you ever begin to wonder if God loves you, take a look at the cross. The cross has become a cherished symbol to Christians of the incredible love of God.

God's Promises

To experience victory in spite of difficult circumstances, you must believe that God will do all He promises. 2 Corinthians 1:20 says: _"For no matter how many promises God has made, they are "Yes" in Christ."_ If you are a Christian, God has made many promises to you. If you ask for any of these, God's answer is always "yes!" _In the Scripture to the right, notice what God is ready to give, if you are willing to receive._ He _will_ express His promises experientially in your life.

> "And my God will meet all your needs according to his glorious riches in Christ Jesus." **Philippians 4:19**

> "I tell you the truth, if you have faith as small as a mustard seed, you can say to this mountain, 'Move from here to there' and it will move. Nothing will be impossible for you." **Matthew 17:20**

• Using one sentence for each, summarize the promise God makes to you:

Philippians 4:19 _____

_____

Matthew 17:20 _____

_____

James 1:5 _____

_____

> "If any of you lacks wisdom, he should ask God, who gives generously to all without finding fault, and it will be given to him." **James 1:5**

Questions:

• Do you believe God can do this in _your_ situation? _____

• Are you experiencing these promises right now? If not, why not?

_____

The Storms of Life

Horatio G. Spafford was a devout Presbyterian businessman in Chicago. He enjoyed a close relationship with D.L. Moody and other Christian leaders of that period. During the Chicago Fire of 1871, Spafford lost a fortune in real estate. Just before this, he had suffered the tragic loss of his only son. Seeking some rest, and wanting to assist D.L. Moody in his evangelistic campaigns in Great Britain, Spafford booked passage aboard the *Ville de Havre* for Europe. A last-minute business development detained him so his wife set sail with their four daughters, with the assurance that Horatio would soon follow. On November 22, the ship collided with the *Lochearn*, an English ship, and sank in 12 minutes. All four Spafford children drowned. Several days later when the survivors had reached Cardiff, Wales, Mrs. Spafford wired her husband, "Saved alone." Spafford took the next ship and as he sailed past the spot where his children had died, God comforted him in a way he had never experienced before. In the midst of his terrible loss, God poured out love upon him, reminding him of the eternal, heavenly joy that had already been granted to each of his children. Spafford was inspired to write a poem that later became a hymn, entitled, *It Is Well With My Soul*. In part, it says: *"When peace, like a river attendeth my way, When sorrows like sea billows roll; Whatever my lot, Thou hast taught me to say, It is well, it is well with my soul. Tho' Satan should buffet, tho' trials should come, Let this blest assurance control, that Christ has regarded my helpless estate and hath shed His own blood for my soul."* This great testimony in song has inspired and encouraged thousands and is still sung today in churches around the world.[1]

Questions:

• If you are presently going through a difficult time, are you letting God redeem your worst crises for His glory? How are you doing that?

_____

• How are you preparing for the crises you will inevitably face?

_____

Four Good Reasons to Trust God

Four truths that affect the way I view God in the midst of crises are:

1. God is love: He always gives what is best for me.
2. God is all-knowing: His word for my life is always right.
3. God is all-powerful: He will always meet my need.
4. God never changes: I can trust Him in every circumstance.

Questions:

• Do you know God this way? _____

• Which one of these truths do you struggle to believe? Why?

_____

• What did God say to you during your study today?

_____

• What will you do as a result?

_____

Try and write the "four truths" about God from memory in the space to the right.

LESSON 2
Crises Promote Gaining Life By Losing It
Losing His Life

I was recently challenged by the testimony of Dr. Joseph Tson. Joseph was the pastor of Second Baptist Church, Oradea, Romania, during the years of intense communist oppression. On several occasions he was arrested and subjected to long periods of brutal interrogation. During an interrogation in Ploiesti, he was threatened with death if he did not cooperate with the authorities. Joseph replied, "Your supreme weapon is killing. My supreme weapon is dying." He told his captors that his sermons had been recorded on cassette tapes and that he had written tracts to encourage his fellow Christians. He noted that if he were to be executed, people would know he had truly believed what he had said and had been willing to die for his beliefs. Thus they would be far more interested in hearing what he had preached. Joseph concluded that the best thing that could happen to him and his message would be his execution!

His captors decided *not* to execute him, as that would defeat their purpose! Joseph recounted later, "I remember how for many years I had been afraid of dying. Because I wanted badly to live, I wasted my life in inactivity. But now that I had placed my life on the altar and decided I was ready to die for the gospel, they were telling me they would not kill me! As long as I tried to save my life, I was losing it. Now that I was willing to lose it, I found it."[2]

When Jesus guided His disciples to experience God, His teaching often ran contrary to the world's. *Look carefully at His profound words in the Scripture to the right.*

Questions:
• How do you "save" your life? _____

• How do you "lose" your life? _____

• How did Jesus illustrate this principle?

_____

• Are you presently trying to "save" your life or have you given it entirely to Christ?

_____

The world teaches that you should always strive to "save" yourself. That is, never place yourself in a situation where you might be hurt; don't give yourself to others, but seek all the affirmation and pleasures that you can. Our society encourages you to affirm self. Jesus said to deny self. Popular psychology says man's greatest problem today is

> "I tell you the truth, unless a kernel of wheat falls to the ground and dies, it remains only a single seed. But if it dies, it produces many seeds. The man who loves his life will lose it, while the man who hates his life in this world will keep it for eternal life."
> **John 12:24-25**

low self-esteem. Jesus cautions that your problem is you think too much of yourself.

If you are living with the attitude of "saving" your life, then you will be constantly disappointed. For example, if you believe that a Christian should not experience pain, your life will be in constant turmoil because this world holds suffering. If you think God only wants to give you the material desires of your heart, then losing your job will be disastrous! If your focus is on this world and you feel God "owes" you and your family a long and healthy life, then when illness and death come, you will be devastated. Many of our crises come because we assume things that are not true.

Question:
• Are any of the above assumptions a factor in your life? *Explain in the space to the left.*

A Matter of Trust
Tammy, a young nursing student in my church, faced a critical point in her life. She was nearing graduation and had no prospect of marriage. All her life she had desired and planned for marriage. Now, time seemed to be racing by and God had not answered her earnest prayers for a husband. Her dreams seemed to be crumbling when she came to me for counsel. I shared Romans 8:32 which says: *"He who did not spare his own Son, but gave him up for us all—how will he not also, along with him, graciously give us all things?"* I told her I would pray for her. But I challenged her, "If God, in His infinite wisdom and perfect love, should decide it is best for you *not* to marry, could you trust Him and accept this?" Tammy was a faithful Christian, but getting married was very important to her. Ultimately, she decided that she could trust God completely with her future, whether she was married or single. She later shared with me that God had given her peace and contentment regardless of her marital status.

She "lost her life" to God, releasing even her most treasured hope. Wouldn't you know it? Soon after that, a fine Christian student joined our church. I performed their wedding and they now have two beautiful children. By losing her life to God, Tammy saved it.

The Cost of Obedience
There is no such thing as "Christianity without cost." Read Philippians 2:5-11.

• How would you describe Jesus' attitude?
_____

• What did Jesus "give up" in order to obey His Father?
_____

• What was the result Jesus' suffering?
_____
_____

• How can you follow Jesus' example?
_____

• How would your life change if you adopted the mind of Christ?

_____

_____

Consider the trials Jesus endured. His home had been heaven. Yet Jesus did not regard this position as a "right" or condition that He should hold on to. He did not have the attitude that God the Father "owed" this to Him! When God's will was for His Son to give up everything, Jesus accepted the assignment. He was obedient, even to the point of an excruciating and humiliating death. No mathematician could calculate the distance from the right hand of God to the cross. None of us will ever experience such an extreme change in circumstance. What was the result of Jesus' obedience in crisis? His heavenly Father exalted Him to the highest place and He will be worshipped forever. His life will bring salvation to billions and His obedience will bring glory to the Father like no other act in all eternity.

Questions:

Which of the following situations could you entrust to God? Circle them.

loss of job

parents' divorce

a sibling addicted to drugs

death of a loved one

chronic health problems

other _____

bankruptcy

an impossible task

betrayal from someone you trusted

flunking out of college

abuse

The Cost of Discipleship

Dietrich Bonhoeffer was an outstanding young pastor and theologian in Germany. He had a brilliant mind and was attaining international prominence when Adolph Hitler came to power. In 1937 he wrote the famous book, *The Cost of Discipleship*, which challenged Christians not to settle for a superficial religion but to strive for absolute loyalty and obedience to Christ. Bonhoeffer was deeply disturbed by what Hitler was doing in Germany and strenuously opposed it. This caused him to lose his church and to be ostracized by many of Germany's religious and political leaders. As pressures mounted, friends in the United States enticed him to come and deliver a series of lectures in order to get him out of Germany before the war began. Soon, however, Bonhoeffer felt compelled to return to his homeland.

After his return, he became involved in rescuing Jewish people and was eventually implicated in a plot to assassinate Hitler. While imprisoned, he ministered to fellow prisoners, many on death row, through his prayers, exhortation, and personal example of trust in God. One Sunday, as he led a worship service for his companions, Gestapo guards came and took Bonhoeffer away. His last words to those in the service were: "This is the end, for me, the beginning of life." The next morning, on April 9, 1945, Bonhoeffer was hung at the execution shed in Flossenburg concentration camp, only three weeks before Hitler committed suicide. The doctor who witnessed his execution declared, "In the almost fifty years that I have worked as a doctor, I have hard-

"To this you were called, because Christ suffered for you, leaving you an example, that you should follow in his steps. "He committed no sin, and no deceit was found in his mouth." When they hurled their insults at him, he did not retaliate; when he suffered, he made no threats. Instead, he entrusted himself to him who judges justly. He himself bore our sins in his body on the tree, so that we might die to sins and live for righteousness; by his wounds you have been healed."

1 Peter 2:21-24

ly ever seen a man die so entirely submissive to the will of God." After the war's end, Bonhoeffer's writings were widely distributed and gained a more serious reading in light of his devotion and martyrdom. To this day, books like *The Cost of Discipleship* have challenged Christians around the world including me and my children.[3]

Questions:
• What do you need to submit to God in order to be *entirely* committed to Christ the way Bonhoeffer was? _____

Notice the example of Jesus in the Scripture to the left.

Questions:
• To what have Christians been "called?"

_____

• *To the left, list the trials Jesus endured.*

• What was the result of Jesus' obedience to His Father?

_____

God's primary concern is not that we live a trial-free life. If this were so, He would take us to heaven immediately upon conversion. Rather, He desires to use us in His plan to bring sinful humanity to Himself. For this reason He leaves us in an imperfect world, where we are not immune to suffering. It's like a doctor who works on the front lines of a battlefield. The wounded and dying desperately need him there, but this puts him in danger. Likewise, we live in a spiritual battlefield where good people suffer.

Questions:
• Have you experienced the cost of following Jesus? How?

_____

• What might it cost you for God to bring redemption to:
   your family? _____
   your workplace? _____
   your children? _____
   the world? _____

• What might it cost you *not* to be obedient to what God is telling you?

_____

Facing the Flame
One of my favorite Old Testament stories is that of Shadrach, Meshach, and Abednego. These men lived in a pagan society that worshipped idols. When a law was issued that every person must worship an idol, these three refused, despite enormous pressure. *Take your Bible and read carefully their bold statement of faith to the king who threatened to throw them*

to their deaths in a flaming furnace (Daniel 3:16-18).

Questions:
• Was their faith based on God delivering them from their crisis? How do you know?

_____

• What was the outcome of their faithfulness?

_____

What an incredible act of faith! These young men were faithful to God even when those around them were not. What was the reward for their faithfulness? A death threat! But notice their response. They said, we know God *could* deliver us from this crisis, *but whether He does or not* makes no difference to us. Our faithfulness to God is not based on whether or not He protects us from hardship. It is based on the fact that we know He is God and we know He loves us.

Write a prayer right now in the space to the right, releasing your life to God, giving up any "rights" you have been clinging to.

Questions:
• Are you trying to serve God on your terms or have you completely released your life to Him? What is the evidence of this?

_____

• What areas of your life do you still need to release to God?

_____

_____

• What did God say to you during your study today?

_____

• What will you do as a result?

_____

_____

LESSON 3
Crises Prove the Sincerity of Faith

For the record, five-year-old Julius Rosenberg is NOT afraid of bears. Of course, grandiose pronouncements by young children are generally taken with a grain of salt. But on Sunday, September 20, 1992, Julius discovered he really *wasn't* afraid! He was on the edge of a dock at his family's cottage at West Hawk Lake with his three year old sister Barbara, when a black bear approached them. The children jumped into the water but the bear followed them, catching Barbara's life jacket in its mouth. Julius turned and tugged on his sister until the bear released its grip. Julius then "stared down" the bear, even giving it a fierce growl! The children fled into their cottage where Julius shouted "A bear bit Barbie, mommy. The bear bit Barbie." Their mother saw the bear coming and frantically closed two doors behind the fleeing children to prevent the hungry bear from entering the cottage. No one who knew Julius would have imagined him staring down a hungry bear. But a "crisis" had dramatically confirmed his belief. Julius was *not* afraid of bears!

Crises bring the opportunity to prove what you *really* believe about God. *Notice in the Scripture to the left what a storm at sea demonstrated about the disciples' faith.*

Questions:
• With Jesus present, were the disciples *really* perishing?

_____

• What did they learn about Jesus *because* of this crisis? Were they stronger disciples as a result? How?

_____

_____

• Are you presently facing a crisis? What pressure is it bringing to bear?

_____

• Have you turned to Jesus? What have you learned about Him?

_____

Until now, you may have lived a sheltered life. Perhaps your parents carried the load for you in difficult times. But now you may be exposed to things you never encountered before. You are beginning a stage of life where crises can become more frequent and severe. Are you prepared for them when they come? How will you respond?

Facing Death
The doctor approached me and in a somber tone said, "Mr. Blackaby, your wife is critically ill. We will have to do immediate surgery. It's serious enough that we may not be able to save her." When they took her away to the operating room, I was left alone with God. The pressure of that moment led me quickly to my relationship with God. We had five children; our daughter was only a few months old. Would God intervene? If He did, how would my family and I live the rest of our lives? Casually? Intensely? This crisis led me to a stronger, more focused relationship with God and His purpose for me and my family. I have sought to live with this intensity ever since. We have never experienced so much of the goodness and faithfulness of God as we have in the ensuing years!

Take your Bible and read what Jesus said in Matthew 11:28-30.

"One day Jesus said to his disciples, 'Let's go over to the other side of the lake.' So they got into a boat and set out. As they sailed, he fell asleep. A squall came down on the lake, so that the boat was being swamped, and they were in great danger. The disciples went and woke him, saying, 'Master, Master, we're going to drown!' He got up and rebuked the wind and the raging waters; the storm subsided, and all was calm. 'Where is your faith?' he asked his disciples. In fear and amazement they asked one another, 'Who is this? He commands even the winds and the water, and they obey him.'"
Luke 8:22-25

Questions:
• Who does Jesus invite to come to Him?

_____

• What does Jesus do when you come to Him in your crises?

_____

Jesus encourages His followers to turn to Him when the hard times hit. He is not disinterested, letting you work out your problems for yourself. He is not powerless, unable to do anything for you. He is not out of touch: unable to understand what you are going through. He is "gentle and humble" and He *is* able to bring "rest" to your soul. He may not always change your circumstance, but He will bring a peace to your heart even in the midst of the most difficult situations if you will trust Him.

Bitter or Better?

Bob was extremely bitter. His father had been an abusive alcoholic. As a young boy, Bob would cry himself to sleep praying that God would change his father. Now as a young man, he came to me and said, "My father died an alcoholic." I heard the bitterness in his voice. He had determined that he would have nothing more to do with God. His life reflected that decision. Yet it was obvious that he desperately longed for the love and peace of God. I shared with Bob that God loved his father even more than he did. If God is true to His description in the Bible, He would have been reaching out to Bob's father day after day, urging him to turn from his alcoholism and to let Him change his life. We read passages of Scripture where God urged people to turn to Him and receive healing. Now it was Bob's turn. Would he allow God to heal *his* brokeness?

Question:
• Do you have bitterness in your life? If so, what do you think God wants you to do about it?

_____

_____

Paul's Sufferings

Look up 2 Corinthians 4:7-11 and 11:23-28 and list a few things Paul endured during his Christian life.

_____

_____

_____

Questions:
• How do Paul's sufferings compare with yours?

_____

• If Paul underwent such suffering, why do you think he continued to faithfully serve God?

_____

Jesus encourages His followers to turn to Him when the hard times hit. He is not disinterested, letting you work out your problems for yourself.

100
50
0

"Who shall separate us from the love of Christ? Shall trouble or hardship or persecution or famine or nakedness or danger or sword?. . . No, in all these things we are more than conquerors through him who loved us. For I am convinced that neither death nor life, neither angels nor demons, neither the present nor the future, nor any powers, neither height nor depth, nor anything else in all creation, will be able to separate us from the love of God that is in Christ Jesus our Lord."

Romans 8:35, 37-39

Few people have endured the hardships Paul did. His biography reads like a litany of everything that can possibly go wrong in a Christian's life! *Yet this is the same person who wrote the Scriptures to the left.*

Questions:

• How confident was Paul that God could give him victory in every circumstance?
❑ Somewhat   ❑ Absolutely

• Circle the things Paul said could NEVER separate us from the love of God.

• Was Paul confident that God would always change his situation? What *was* his confidence in?

Paul was convinced God could bring victory in *every* circumstance. Paul had experienced enough hardships to know what he was talking about. Yet, Paul's confidence was not in the expectation that if he prayed, God would remove his difficulties. After all, even Jesus did not have His "cup" of suffering taken from Him in the Garden of Gethsemane (Luke 22:41-44). Instead, Paul firmly trusted that *nothing* could ever separate him from the love of God. As long as Paul was experiencing the presence of Christ in his life, he could boldly face the most devastating situations.

Helen Keller

The story of Helen Keller is a testimony to the faithfulness of God. Helen grew up unable to hear or speak or see. God brought a teacher, Mrs. Armstrong, to help her. With great difficulty, Helen began to turn to God. Because of her unique limitations, she came to know God in ways most people never do. As an adult, she was able to encourage thousands of hurting people to find assurance and comfort in a relationship with God. Toward the end of her life she was asked: "If you could live your life over again, would you want it to be any different?" Her answer was "no," for through her crises, she had come to know God so intimately, to experience His love so deeply, and to "see" God so clearly, she would never trade her relationship with God for anything!

Crises will make you bitter or better. If you will release your life to God and accept His will for you as an expression of His perfect love, then God will take you to a depth of relationship with Him that you could not have otherwise experienced.

Questions:

• Name someone in your circle of friends who is currently in a crisis. Briefly describe his or her problem in the space available.

• Is God inviting you to minister to them? If so, what will you commit to do for them?

• What did God say to you during your study today?

_____

_____

• What will you do as a result?

_____

_____

_____

LESSON 4
Crises Prepare Us for Greater Assignments

Roy Whetstine was a gemmologist from Texas. In 1986 he visited a gem-and-mineral bazaar in Tucson, Arizona. There he spotted an egg-sized violet and blue rock in a Tupperware container, priced at $15. Whetstine offered the owner $10 and the rock was his. He suspected, however, that there was more to this rock than the vendor had realized. After months of appraising it, he determined that the rock was actually a 1,905 carat star sapphire with an estimated uncut value of 2.28 million dollars! One man's junk *is* another man's treasure. The rock had not changed. The difference was in the eye of the beholder. Likewise, crises can be seen in different ways. Some view them as negative, to be avoided at all cost. Others regard them as opportunities for personal and spiritual growth.

There is no greater challenge than a God-sized assignment. That is, any task God gives you that only He is capable of carrying out. Such assignments not only reveal your character but also help to develop it.

Would *you* like a God-sized assignment? Are you sure? God-sized tasks are costly. Jesus paid an incredible price to obey His Father. God does not give big assignments to little characters. He looks for someone with a "big" character and matches His assignment to them. Jesus' mission involved suffering. Read carefully the amazing verses to the right.

Questions:
• How did Jesus pray to His Father?

_____

• Why did God allow Jesus to suffer?

_____

• What is an aspect of your character that might be "perfected" through suffering?

_____

• Would you be willing to undergo suffering if it made you a stronger Christian? Why or why not?

_____

"During the days of Jesus' life on earth, he offered up prayers and petitions with loud cries and tears to the one who could save him from death, and he was heard because of his reverent submission. Although he was a son, he learned obedience from what he suffered and, once made perfect, he became the source of eternal salvation for all who obey him." **Hebrews 5:7-9**

• Are you willing to "pay any price" for God to use you mightily in His kingdom? Think about evidence in your life which reflects this commitment.

Scripture says Jesus prayed with loud cries and tears to His Father who had the power to save Him from death. God heard Him but allowed Him to suffer. In ways too profound for us to comprehend, Jesus was "perfected" through His suffering. The word "perfect" also means "complete." For reasons known only to God, Jesus had to suffer if He was to be the Redeemer of mankind. The Son of God had already demonstrated perfect obedience by leaving heaven and walking upon the earth sinlessly, and now He was obedient even when it meant death on a cross. The perfecting process was painful but the assignment was enormous!

Questions:
• Do members of your family need salvation? Name one in the space to the left.

• Do your friends need freedom from spiritual bondage? Name two.

• What kind of person would you need to be for God to save them through your influence?

_____

• What attitudes, habits, or beliefs does God have to "perfect" before He can use you?

_____

• Would you be willing to let Him do so in order to see salvation come to those around you? ❑ Yes ❑ No, not at this time.

What matters to God when involving people in His work is *character*. One way God develops character is through *suffering*. James encouraged us. Note the Scripture to the left.

Questions:
• How does James say we should view our trials? _____

• Is James referring to only one specific kind of suffering? _____

• What can be the results of our going through trials?

_____

This counsel from James directly contradicts what we would naturally think. We tend to think that only a masochist would experience "joy" in trials. Yet James says it can be done! In fact, he said to consider it "pure" joy, that is, joy without any reservation or qualification. Why? Because the "tests" we go through make us learn perseverance. If you learn to persevere as a Christian, you will become complete and mature, lacking nothing for this life. Ultimately your perseverance will earn you a reward in heaven. These are good reasons for welcoming various trials.

"Consider it pure joy, my brothers, whenever you face trials of many kinds, because you know that the testing of your faith develops perseverance. Perseverance must finish its work so that you may be mature and complete, not lacking anything. . . . Blessed is the man who perseveres under trial, because when he has stood the test, he will receive the crown of life that God has promised to those who love him." **James 1:2-4, 12**

Difficult Assignments

One of the things I enjoy most about my work is the opportunity to travel to mission fields around the world to encourage foreign missionaries. Inevitably I come away challenged by their lives. I met some fine missionary families in the Ukraine where the Chernobyl nuclear power plant disaster occurred spreading deadly radiation over the land. This catastrophe has been linked to over 4,300 deaths and has affected over 3.5 million people. The missionaries serving in that area knew that the water they drank and the food they ate could quite likely be contaminated by radiation. Yet, they also knew that someone had to go and share the Gospel with these people who faced this danger daily. The missionary families recognized that God's assignment for them was difficult, and might involve suffering, but they stayed to encourage the people and glorify God.

I met with missionaries serving in war-torn countries in Africa. Many were in mortal danger. With a heavy heart I watched these dedicated people preparing to enter rebel-infested areas where missionaries had already been murdered. God has an assignment for every Christian. Not all will be called as foreign missionaries. Not all will be called to endure suffering to the same degree. Yet *every* call of God involves a cross (Matthew 16:24). You cannot follow Christ without taking up your cross. When you face suffering and hardship, will your character and relationship to Christ be of such quality that He can entrust you with His assignment?

Saul and David

There is a fascinating contrast between the first two kings of Israel. Saul was the first king. *Notice his background in 1 Samuel 9:1-2.*

Saul was a strong and handsome man from a respected family. From the outward perspective, Saul seemed like the perfect choice for king. Yet, his reign was disastrous. He became jealous of anyone who received more praise than he did (1 Samuel 18:6-9; 28-29). Saul had a violent temper and was prone to fits of anger (1 Samuel 18:10-12). He became so bitter that he betrayed those who had saved his life and murdered innocent priests who displeased him (1 Samuel 24:16-22; 22). Saul grew so conceited that he presumed he could perform the role of priest and blatantly disobey a word from God (1 Samuel 15). Saul's life ended in defeat, failure, utter humiliation, and suicide.

David, however, had a different beginning. As a youth, he fought lions and bears to defend his father's sheep (1 Samuel 17:37). David's first public assignment from God was to face the terrible giant, Goliath (1 Samuel 17:41-49). David's life was filled with hardship as a young adult. He was in constant danger with many attempts on his life; his wife grew to despise him for his devotion to God (2 Samuel 6:20); his closest friend was separated from him and eventually killed (1 Samuel 20:41-42); many of his good friends and spiritual advisers died (1 Samuel 22:11-19); his wife and possessions were stolen from him (1 Samuel 30:1-6); he lived in caves and even had to feign insanity in order to survive (1 Samuel 21:13). David lived with the frustration of knowing that God wanted him to be king, yet having to wait for years while watching the incompetent King Saul tear the country apart.

Whereas Saul had a relatively easy road toward the monarchy, he did not have the character to flourish in that exalted position. David, however, faced incredible ad-

In order for God to accomplish a difficult work, He sometimes requires suffering. As it was necessary for His Son to suffer, so at times, it is necessary for us to suffer as well.

versity in his spiritual pilgrimage. Yet, when he became king, he governed as the greatest king ever to rule in Israel. David ruled with compassion and fairness, and when he sinned, unlike Saul, he was sincerely humbled and penitent. He did not exalt himself, but God. He did not rule with an iron fist like Saul. God had refined his character so that he would be fit for a significant assignment.

Questions:
• Would you be willing for God to bring you through adversity so that He could develop your character and give you a larger assignment? _____

• How is God changing your faith in Him and your character through what you are enduring?

_____

In order for God to accomplish a difficult work, He sometimes requires suffering. As it was necessary for His Son to suffer, so at times, it is necessary for us to suffer as well. Paul declared: *"I want to know Christ and the power of his resurrection and the fellowship of sharing in his sufferings, becoming like him in his death"* (Philippians 3:10).

Questions:
• Could you honestly pray that you *want* to share in the sufferings of Jesus as Paul did?

_____

• What did God say to you during your study today?

_____

_____

• What will you do as a result?

_____

LESSON 5:
Making Adjustments to God When Life Looks "Dark"
A Blessing in Disguise

Corrie Ten Boom in her book, *The Hiding Place,* tells the amazing story of when she and her sister Betsie were transferred to the notorious Ravensbruck concentration camp during World War II. As the sisters attempted to go to sleep their first night in Barracks 28, they were repeatedly bitten by fleas. When Betsie prayed and thanked God for their accommodations, including the fleas, Corrie thought she had gone too far! "There's no way even God can make me thankful for a flea" said Corrie. Yet, as they adjusted to their life in that horrible death camp, they noticed a strange thing happening. Despite the usual thoroughness of their German prison guards, the Bible they had smuggled in to the barracks was never discovered. Each night the two Christian sisters would read the Bible aloud. More and more women listened until eventually the entire barracks of broken and fearful women was clinging desperately to every word. The readings were then translated by the prisoners into all the European languages represented in the camp. The Bible reading became so popular they had to have two different readings every night. Still, the guards did not find their Bible or intervene in their meetings.

One day the sisters discovered the reason the prison guards had not entered their quarters. The fleas! The guards did not want to catch them, so they neglected to search the flea-infested barracks. Those tiny creatures of God were actually guarding these women from the mighty German army![4]

God had a difficult assignment. Those abused and discouraged women desperately needed to hear His message of hope and peace, and He needed messengers who would be willing to endure severe deprivations. In the midst of their crisis, Corrie and Betsie had to make enormous adjustments in their lives, but the result was that salvation and hope came to many who were only moments from death.

Crises create "moments of decision" which affect the rest of your life. God is always present in those dark moments and ready to teach you in the "way that leads to life" (Matthew 7:13-14). In David's darkest moments, he turned to God for strength and help. *Notice what he says in the Scripture to the right.*

Questions:
• What did David do in his time of his distress?

_____

• How did God respond?

_____

• How do you think this affected the way David worshipped and served God?

_____

• How does David's experience encourage you?

_____

Carrie's Cancer
God gave Marilynn and me four wonderful boys. Our youngest child is our daughter Carrie. She added so much joy to our home. She filled our home with the music of her singing and piano playing. She cheered for her brothers in hockey. Then, when she was 16, the doctors diagnosed her with an advanced case of cancer. She was immediately scheduled for massive doses of chemotherapy, followed by radiation. A bewildering darkness came over us. We turned instinctively to God and waited for a word from Him. The wait seemed endless, yet we knew He would comfort and direct us. *Then from our study of God's word and the encouragement from others came the word in the Scripture to the right.*

This seemed to be God's message to us and to Carrie. God did heal her through His grace. Her restored health brought glory to God and many continue to be en-

"I sought the Lord, and he answered me; he delivered me from all my fears. Those who look to him are radiant; their faces are never covered with shame. This poor man called, and the Lord heard him; he saved him out of all his troubles. The angel of the Lord encamps around those who fear him, and he delivers them. Taste and see that the Lord is good; blessed is the man who takes refuge in him. Fear the Lord, you his saints, for those who fear him lack nothing. The lions may grow weak and hungry, but those who seek the Lord lack no good thing."
Psalm 34:4-10

Jesus said, "This sickness will not end in death. No, it is for God's glory so that God's Son may be glorified through it." **John 11:4**

couraged and strengthened by her testimony. Carrie is now in seminary preparing to serve her Lord in missions.

In times of darkness, Marilynn and I have chosen to turn to God, and He has been gracious to show us His ways. We sought first to respond in trust and obedience. Each time God has taken us through a crisis, it has called for major adjustments in us and in our walk with Him. But in every case, we have come to a fresh understanding of God and how He wants to work with us. Each time we have been able to take what God has taught us and encourage others.

When times of bewilderment overwhelm you, how you respond will affect your life deeply. Some people withdraw or drop out; others worry and fret, even to the point of becoming sick; still others become angry and bitter. But others turn quietly and persistently to God and wait before Him until He hears their cry and delivers them; they are forever strengthened in their walk with God and they become more faithful servants of His.

Questions:
• Are you presently in, or have you gone through a "dark" time? Describe it in the space to the left.

• How does God bring "light" to your difficult times?

_____

Jesus' Example
Read carefully Jesus' prayer in Gethsemane and see how He dealt with the most difficult hours. Take your Bible and read Matthew 26:36-46 and Hebrews 5:7-10.

Questions:
• How does the way *you* handle crises compare with the way Jesus dealt with them?

_____

• Do you have friends, as Jesus did, to "watch with you" while you carry your heavy load? _____

• What do you need to "turn over" to God right now? Write a prayer to God in the space to the left giving all your concerns and difficulties to God right now.

• What did God say to you during your study today?

_____

• What will you do as a result?

_____

[1]Kenneth W. Osbeck, *101 Hymn Stories* (Grand Rapids: Kregel Publications, 1982), 127.
[2]"Thank you for the Beating" Christian Herald April 1988,
[3]*Christian History*, "Dietrich Bonhoeffer" Issue 32 (vol. X, no. 4).
[4]*The Hiding Place*, 180-181.

INTRODUCTION

While Richard was a university student, our church had a "Secret Valentine Week." Everyone drew a name and then sent anonymous notes of encouragement throughout the week. The person who drew Richard's name must have left town because he never received a thing. Richard drew the name of Mrs. Abriel. As a young, single, university student, there were several female names Richard hoped to draw, but the name of an elderly widow living in a rest home was not on his list. Although Richard had often seen Mrs. Abriel at church, he had never talked with her. Swallowing his disappointment, Richard visited her at the senior's residence and, to his surprise, quite enjoyed her company.

During their visit, Richard discovered Mrs. Abriel did not have a regular ride to church; he volunteered to pick her up each Sunday. She had experienced much hardship in her life but had developed a kind, gentle spirit. She would periodically send him encouraging notes and gifts. One weekend, Richard went out of town and forgot to tell Mrs. Abriel. When he apologized for his thoughtlessness, she smiled graciously. She told him she had spent a pleasant Sunday morning visiting with people in the rest home lobby while waiting to be picked up. One day Richard received word that Mrs. Abriel had suffered a stroke and was in intensive care in the hospital. He had never been to ICU before and was intimidated by the somber atmosphere. When Mrs. Abriel saw him arrive, she gave a big smile and apologized for being an inconvenience! She thanked him profusely for the time he had taken to visit her. Only a few hours later, Mrs. Abriel passed into eternity.

As a university student, Richard had no idea what a joy it would be to befriend a senior citizen in his church. Her sweet spirit in the midst of her loneliness and pain left an indelible impression upon him and gave him a new appreciation for senior adults. Richard came to understand that belonging to a church family affords opportunities to develop friendships with saints of God of every age who will greatly enrich your life.

God's invitation to you, not only as a student but for the rest of your life, is to join with God's people as He works to redeem a lost world. It is in the midst of the people of God that He refines and develops your character and sends you on mission to the world.

MEMORY VERSE:

"By this all men will know that you are my disciples, if you love one another."

John 13:35

THIS WEEK'S LESSONS:

Lesson 1
Together in Interdependence

Lesson 2
Together in One Body

Lesson 3
Together in Caring

Lesson 4
Together in Fellowship

Lesson 5
Together in Missions

LESSON 1
Together in Interdependence
What Was Missing?

Derrick had applied to medical school twice; both applications were denied. Bewildered, he came to me for counsel. We agreed we would both pray and search the Scriptures for direction. Had God closed the door? Was there something lacking in his walk with God? Should he re-apply? Only God could answer these questions. Derrick returned later and assured me that: 1) God had not "closed the door"; he was certain God wanted him in medicine; 2) God had given him peace. I sensed something further. I noticed he had not asked his church to pray with him, so we could all experience God's grace through him. He agreed and asked the church to pray. As he once again took the qualifying exams, we all prayed earnestly. This time he passed and entered medical school. Our whole church came to experience new dimensions of confidence in the love and faithfulness of God. Derrick had thought school was something you do on your own. He learned through this experience that as a Christian he was interdependent. He needed others and others needed him. God has made us social beings. That is, we function best when we work *with* others.

1. Sin's destruction.

Studies consistently reveal that one of the chief maladies today is loneliness. Sin isolates! Take your Bible and read Genesis 3:6-24 and Genesis 4:8.

Questions:

• From these verses, list eight consequences of man's sin on a separate piece of paper.

• Look at your list, how many relationships were affected by sin? _____

• Does *every* sin have this potential for harm? Why or why not?

_____

There is nothing as devastating to the human experience as sin. The first sin, as recorded in Scripture, introduced isolation and separation. Husband and wife now: 1) felt awkward about their intimacy; 2) hid from God, suddenly ashamed to be in His presence; 3) began to blame each other rather than accept responsibility for their failure. Tragically the Garden of Eden, once a place of intimacy with God, was now closed to mankind. There would subsequently be pain in childbirth. Children would bring heartache to their parents. Animosity developed between brothers which led to history's first murder. Sin separates people from those who could enrich their lives. *Every* sin carries this devastating potential. Sin attacks your relationships—with God, with your family, with your friends, with your neighbors. Sin leads you to be *independent* rather than *interdependent*. Sin puts all of creation "out of joint."

I've counseled college students who lived in the midst of some of the largest campuses and cities in North America and yet were terribly lonely. Many have wept because of their isolation despite belonging to large families or being surrounded by hundreds of other students. Many notorious murderers and violent criminals have been described as "loners"—they kept to themselves without counsel or accountability and developed attitudes that were highly destructive to themselves and society. God created mankind with an innate need for "togetherness." Our identity and meaning in life are found in the context of our relationships with others. God's invitation is to vital interdependence in the corporate life of His people. This is experienced in many forms, but pre-eminently in a local church body.

Questions:
• Do you have a sense of interdependence with others or do you feel isolated?

_____

• Has sin alienated you from someone? If so, how?

_____

• Do you find it easy or difficult to be transparent with others? Why?

_____

Sin affirms *self* and *independence*, leading to isolation and heartache. But God affirms interdependence, giving and receiving love and forgiveness. These lead to our fulfillment, interrelatedness, and mutual significance. Among the people of God you do not *lose* your identity, as secular critics will try to convince you, but rather it is *in* the group that your true identity is realized.

2. God's remedy.
No one is more aware of the pain that sin brings to *your* relationships than God. That's why He set in motion His plan of redemption. *In the Scripture to the right, notice God's pattern for a new society, one based on peoples' relationship to Him.*

Questions:
• What terms does this Scripture use to describe the people of God?

_____

_____

• In what ways are they different than before? List them in the space to the right.

In Peter's letter to the churches, he focused on the *corporate interdependence* of the people of God. Each Christian had an identity as part of God's people. The term "priesthood of believers" is *always* corporate. Some have distorted this doctrine to say that each person is a priest unto himself and therefore doesn't need others in order to worship and serve God. Biblically, however, this term *always* refers to a *group* of priests. As a Christian, you are one priest, belonging to a priesthood. In the Bible priests were always accountable to one another and functioned together to assist God's people as a whole to be on mission with God.

"But you are a chosen people, a royal priesthood, a holy nation, a people belonging to God, that you may declare the praises of him who called you out of darkness into his wonderful light. Once you were not a people, but now you are the people of God; once you had not received mercy, but now you have received mercy." **1 Peter 2:9-10**

A Part of Something Bigger

It is a freeing experience to be interdependent with other believers! It is amazing to see this at work in the church. I have seen lonely students "come alive" as they experienced Christian "family" for the first time. I don't know *how* many crises our church prayed our university students through. Our students had prayer meeting on campus on Monday, Wednesday, and Friday mornings. They would share what they were facing that day and then pray for each other. When an exam was passed, or an application to a program accepted, the group rejoiced! When a music student had a recital, church members went to show their support. When students participated in sporting events, their church cheered them on. When a student returned from a difficult time spent with their family, they would be comforted by calls and visits from church members. When our students went on summer missions, their church family called them and wrote letters, giving a royal welcome when they returned. Whether it was a time of celebration or a time of sorrow, the first place our students wanted to come was to their church! That's because they realized God had made them a vital part of His Body. They needed support from their church family, and they knew others needed their encouragement. This is God's plan: His people, dependent on Him and interdependent on each other.

Questions:

• While in college, can you describe some ways you can be a vital part of God's people, the church? Do it in the space to the left.

• What did God say to you during your study today?

_____

• What will you do as a result?

_____

LESSON 2
Together in One Body

I vividly remember the births of each of my five children. Marilynn and I were thrilled each time God added to our family. Likewise, our church rejoiced every time God added a new member. We were the family of God and we knew it was a sacred moment whenever God blessed us with a new family member.

Notice in the Scripture to the left how Paul described the people of God in 1 Corinthians 12:27.

Question:

• What phrase is used to describe believers? Who is included in this?

_____

"Now you are the body of Christ, and each one of you is a part of it."
1 Corinthians 12:18

When God brought salvation to mankind, He sent us His Son in human form. During that time, people had the awesome privilege of actually seeing, touching, and hearing God (1 John 1). Once Christ ascended to heaven, people could no longer see God in the flesh. Now God takes on physical form by dwelling within His people, the church. The church has become God's new earthly body. This has significant implications. In order to see God today, people are to look to the church. They see God's love by watching how Christians love each other. They see God's power by observing Him do the impossible through His church.

Local churches are the visible expression of the Body of Christ. It is through these local churches that God seeks to carry out His plan to bring salvation to mankind. *In the Scripture to the right, notice what happens, according to Paul, when you "join" a church.*

Question:
• According to this verse, how does God build a church?

_____

• How personally is God involved?

_____

> "But in fact God has arranged the parts in the body, every one of them, just as he wanted them to be." **1 Corinthians 12:18**

God Equips The Church

The churches where I was a pastor took their responsibility to new church members seriously. I would ask each new member to commit to the entire church to allow God to use them to "build up" His church. I would then challenge the other members to encourage and pray for the new member so that together we could function as God's Body and accomplish His purpose.

Each church is His Body and He has particular assignments for it. Since we are now His Body on earth, He will carry out His redemptive work through us. Further, He will equip each church to carry out His assignment. For instance, If God wants to reach the disadvantaged people of a downtown area, He may choose to do so through *your* church. In this case, He will sensitize your church to the need and equip it to minister. God knows what His assignment for each church will be, so He adds members whom He intends to use in these ministries. God places people in churches for a reason. It is so they can do their part as a member of the Body and together, carry out God's assignment for it.

It was always exciting to see who God added to our church. A music student would give her talents to playing the piano during the worship services. A drama student would organize a drama team to enhance our worship. Education students would become Sunday School teachers. A Fine Arts student designed the church brochure and sign. An architecture student planned the addition to our church building. Ministerial students preached in our missions. Other students devoted their energies to working with our youth. Some served as ushers or labored on the church grounds. Some sang in the choir; many served on committees. Students gifted with compassion would volunteer to go to the rest homes and minister to the elderly. Students who had come out of a life of alcohol and drug abuse would lead services in the rescue mission downtown. Each student who joined was challenged to discover why God brought them to our church, and other members would then become involved in the new work that God did through these new members.

Tom's Gift

Our church had several young boys who came from broken homes. God burdened my son Tom's heart for these boys. Tom was especially concerned about those who had no father in their house. He used to take these boys swimming or on various outings. He taught some to play musical instruments and encouraged all of them to live a Christian life that would honor God. He would even volunteer in their schools. There were many boys whose world Tom brightened. Tom became the strong Christian role model these kids desperately needed at a critical time in their lives. There are young men scattered across the world today who still write and visit him when they can. Many have married fine Christian women and have successful careers. Through Tom's concern for these boys, our church developed various ministries to these children and their families. God knew that there were many young boys in the church who needed a friend and role model, so He equipped the church for this ministry through Tom.

When God places you in a local church, you are not merely joining a "religious organization"; you are part of the Living Body of Christ. God puts you in a particular church because He knows you can help that church to fulfill His assignment. You are vital to the Body and the Body is important to you.

No Division

Notice in the Scripture to the left one aspect of this new relationship with God in His Body.

Questions:

• According to this verse, if someone in your church faces a painful situation, how should you respond?

_____

• If someone in your church is experiencing joy or success, how should it affect you?

_____

> "So that there should be no division in the body, but that its parts should have equal concern for each other. If one part suffers, every part suffers with it; if one part is honored, every part rejoices with it."
> **1 Corinthians 12:25-26**

Our church sought to function in a way that reflected the above passage. When Joe graduated from the college of medicine, we held a "fellowship celebration." When Dan won an award in Fine Arts, many attended the art show rejoicing because we were so proud of him. When Debbie's mother died of cancer, we gathered around to give comfort. Brenda was ostracized by her own family for becoming a Christian so we wept with her and surrounded her with the love of Christ. One Sunday evening, a young college couple stood before the church and wept as they confessed their sexual sin. They received forgiveness as those present offered their love and prayed that they would experience restoration. People discovered that as a part of the Body of Christ you do not hurt alone. Likewise, your church family shares your joys and successes. **Take careful note: watching religious programs on television, or reading Christian books, can never *replace* your church family!**

Building Up the Body

Take your Bible and read Ephesians 4:1-3, 11-14 and see how Paul describes the church.

Questions:

• From the verses you read, make a list of ways others "build you up" in the space to the right.

• If you were to leave town for a month, who in your church would be affected? What ministries within your church would suffer because you were not there?

_____

_____

• How might God use you to "build up":

teenagers: _____

students: _____

families:_____

senior adults:_____

• What did God say to you during your study today?

_____

• What will you do as a result?

_____

God puts you in a particular church because He knows you can help that church to fulfill His assignment. You are vital to the Body and the Body is important to you.

100

50

0

LESSON 3
Together in Caring

Bill, a university student, was sitting in church waiting for the service to begin. Across the auditorium sat Mrs. Clark, a tiny, frail woman recently widowed. A thought came to Bill: "Now that Mr. Clark is gone, who will maintain their yard?" Bill dismissed the thought and resumed reading the order of service in the bulletin. The question came again: "Who will help Mrs. Clark?" Bill finally rose and made his way over to Mrs. Clark. When he told her about his concern for the upkeep of her yard, he was taken aback by the look of joy and relief that spread across her face. Mrs. Clark was a gracious English woman who refused to be a burden to anyone. Yet she felt overwhelmed at trying to maintain her large yard without her husband and had been praying that God would send help. In "payment" for Bill's yard work, Mrs. Clark gave him a box of her famous baking which he (and his three roommates) eagerly looked forward to each week. Mrs. Clark became a blessing to these four students even as she had been blessed.

My 10-year-old grandson recently commented, "What do people *do* who don't have a church? I feel sorry for them." He was insightful to realize so young that the church is indispensable for the Christian. In this lesson we will examine three areas where church members can effectively minister to one another.

1. Helping one another.
Take your Bible and read Acts 4:33-34.

Questions:
• How did the church respond to people in need? Why do you think they did this?

_____

_____

• Are you willing to part with your possessions in order to help someone in your church? Why or why not?

_____

_____

• Has someone in your church met a need in your life? *If so, write a brief account of it in the space to the left, and thank God for expressing His love for you through that person.*

No Shortage of Needs
The churches where I was a pastor were always filled with needy people. Muriel was an elderly lady with multiple sclerosis. She was bound to a wheelchair and had great difficulty speaking. Our church family came to know Muriel well enough that they could understand what she was saying and they became actively involved in her life. Our university students saw her as a special person. They would give her rides to church, and there were always those who would sit with her during the service. Students would take her on outings on the weekends. She was often invited to birthday parties. I saw it as no accident that God added several medical students to our church family who understood her condition and were able to minister to her. This lonely woman's life received an enormous blessing from the students at our church, and they grew spiritually as they ministered to her.

We also had several people who were mentally challenged. Some of our church members volunteered to teach a special Bible study and minister to them during the week. Many of our students would go out of their way to befriend those who were neglected at home and in society. These special people found love and acceptance at our church that they had not discovered anywhere else.

College students can be extremely creative! Peter was a student with little money but he wanted to help young families in his church. He designed home-made coupons and gave them as gifts to young parents. His coupons could be redeemed for free baby-sitting, raking leaves, or errands for the busy parents. Peter was allowing the Spirit of God to guide him in practical ways to minister to others in his church.

God blessed us with mature adults who ministered to our university students. We had a Ukrainian lady in our church who loved to cook for them. Some of the meals she served were legendary! There were families who regularly invited international students into their homes for Christmas and other holidays. Some helped students find summer jobs. Many of our students developed friendships with church members that lasted long after their graduation from college. Together as a church, we sought to meet one another's needs.

2. Forgiving one another.
Read the Scripture to the right.

Questions:
• Did people in the first church have conflicts? How do you know?

_____

• How does Scripture say you are to respond to someone with whom you have a "grievance"? _____

• How were church members to respond to someone caught in sin?

_____

• If sin overcomes you, do you have a church family that helps to restore you to wholeness again? If so, how do they do that? Will you trust them to help you?

_____

• What are you doing to help a fellow church member who has a burden?

_____

• How is someone in your church presently helping to carry *your* burden?

_____

The early churches were not immune to conflicts. Yet Paul admonished them to "bear" with one another, making allowances for each other's imperfections. He further instructed them to forgive in the same way Christ forgave them. Anyone who realizes the awesome cost involved for God to forgive their sin will consider it a small thing to forgive the often trivial offenses of others.

3. Praying for one another.
Take your Bible and read James 5:14-16.

Questions:
• According to this passage, why is it important to pray for one another?

_____

• How seriously do you take the prayer concerns of fellow Christians?

_____

• Do you take advantage of opportunities in your student group or church to pray for those who need healing or forgiveness?

_____

"Bear with each other and forgive whatever grievances you may have against one another. Forgive as the Lord forgave you."
Colossians 3:13

"Brothers, if someone is caught in a sin, you who are spiritual should restore him gently. But watch yourself, or you also may be tempted. Carry each other's burdens, and in this way you will fulfill the law of Christ." **Galatians 6:1-2**

There's no better place on earth to share your concerns than with your church family. They can take your needs into the throne room of God and ask for His divine intervention for your life. Miracles have occurred as the result of church prayer meetings! When couples announced their engagement in our church, they would often come before our church and we would commit to pray for them as they approached their marriage. Ivah, an elderly widow, loved to pray. When a student in our church had a difficult assignment or they were going to share the gospel with a friend, they would always alert Ivah so they would have the assurance of her intercession.

Questions:
• *In the space to the left, list the three ways church members can minister to one another.*

• What did God say to you during your study today?

_____

• What will you do as a result?

_____

LESSON 4
Together in Fellowship
In 320 A.D., the Roman Emperor, Licinius, commanded Christians to renounce their faith or be executed. Forty soldiers stationed at Sebaste, Armenia, in the Twelfth Legion refused the command. They were stripped naked and forced out onto a frozen lake. On the shore, Roman soldiers built fires and prepared warm baths for anyone willing to recant and forsake Christianity. In their final hours of life, those 40 believers sang hymns and prayed together. Finally, one of them was so overcome with fear and cold that he fled to the shore. However, a soldier on the shoreline had been so impressed by the dedication and fellowship of the faithful Christians that he ran out to join them, replacing the defector. Their devotion to Christ and their love for one another had been so compelling that an observer was constrained to give his life to Christ. The fellowship between Christians and their God can have a powerful, life-changing influence on others. Students who have participated in such fellowship have had their lives forever changed.[1]

Read the description of the first church God ever established in the Scripture to the left.

Questions:
• What words come to your mind as you read how the first church functioned?

_____

• In Acts 2:42, what four things did the church members devote themselves to? *List them in the space to the right.*

• What evidence suggests the people cared for each other?

_____

"They devoted themselves to the apostles' teaching and to the fellowship, to the breaking of bread and to prayer. Everyone was filled with awe, and many wonders and miraculous signs were done by the apostles. All the believers were together and had everything in common. . . . Every day they continued to meet together in the temple courts. They broke bread in their homes and ate together with glad and sincere hearts, praising God and enjoying the favor of all the people. And the Lord added to their number daily those who were being saved." **Acts 2:42-44, 47**

• How did all of this affect those who were watching them?

_____

Scripture gives a glimpse of how the early churches functioned. They did everything together. They *studied God's Word* together at the feet of the Apostles. They *fellowshipped* together at the temple or in each other's homes. They *broke bread* together. They also *prayed* together. The result was that unbelievers observing them were attracted to what they saw and people were regularly being converted and joining them.

Koinonia

The fact that early Christians met together is not unusual; pagan religions did the same thing. The difference was in the "koinonia" that the first church experienced. The Greek word "*koinonia*" is one of the most exciting words in the New Testament. It means the total interrelatedness in love between God and those He loves. No English word can fully express it. Notice how the Amplified Bible translates it in 1 John 1:3:

> *What we have seen and [ourselves] heard we are also telling you, so that you too may realize and enjoy <u>fellowship</u> as partners and partakers with us. And [this] <u>fellowship</u> that we have (which is a distinguishing mark of Christians) is with the Father and with His Son Jesus Christ, the Messiah.*

Questions:
• What is the distinguishing mark of Christians? _____

• Who do Christians have fellowship with? _____

John was one of Jesus' closest friends. In the above verse John invites *every* person to enjoy an intimate fellowship with God. Notice the close connection between our relationship with God and our relationship with other Christians in the Scripture to the right.

Questions:
• Write the essence of Jesus' prayer in one sentence.

_____

• What is the model for how unified Christians are to be?

_____

• What will be the result of perfect unity among believers?

_____

We cannot fathom the intimacy between God the Father and God the Son. The Father loved His Son with a holy, perfect love. Christ loved His heavenly Father perfectly and was absolutely submissive to His will. Their hearts, minds, and wills were

"That all of them may be one, Father, just as you are in me and I am in you. May they also be in us so that the world may believe that you have sent me. I have given them the glory that you gave me, that they may be one as we are one: I in them and you in me. May they be brought to complete unity to let the world know that you sent me and have loved them even as you have loved me." **John 17:21-23**

in complete harmony. Because of this, Jesus prayed in John 17 that each of His followers would be devoted to God the Father and to the Son in the same way that the Father and Son loved each other.

As Christians experience the incredible, sacrificial love of God, they naturally want to respond in love. Christians have the same heavenly Father and are therefore spiritually, brothers and sisters. It is this mutual relationship to our Lord that leads to a divine fellowship which is *koinonia,* a fellowship we experience with God and with each other.

There are several areas where *koinonia* is expressed in the church. These include prayer, worship, and gathering together.

1. Fellowship in prayer.
A fascinating event occurred in the first church in Acts 12. Notice the Scripture to the left.

Questions:
• What was Peter's situation? _____

• How did the church respond to Peter's dilemma? _____

Peter faced one of the darkest times of his life. Imprisoned by King Herod, he was scheduled to be executed the following morning. The church immediately assembled at the home of John Mark's mother and prayed through the night. As they were praying, Peter knocked on the door! The people were amazed and grew even stronger in their faith in God and their commitment to one another.

A Highlight for Our Students
Prayer meetings were special times of intimacy in our church. College students made up a large percentage of the group that gathered weekly to encourage one another. The gathering would often last two hours or longer. We sat in a circle and searched God's Word for fresh insights for our life together as the Body of Christ. We shared what we saw God doing around us. We were alert to the Holy Spirit as He sensitized our hearts to each other.

We would divide into small groups to pray for one another. Many of our church members shared their burdens for non-Christian parents, family, and friends. Some confessed and repented of their sins and experienced the joy that comes from forgiveness. Others prayed about jobs, school, or relationships. When someone told what they were experiencing, others often felt impressed by the Spirit to pray with them and to encourage them during the week. As the formal prayer time closed, many groups continued to pray. It was not uncommon for students to come to a saving faith in Christ during the prayer meeting. So intimate and exciting was this time that college students would sometimes bring their friends *first* to the prayer meeting before ever inviting them to a worship service!

This experience is God's invitation for His people. Our Lord was present with us, guiding and instructing us in our life together. *His life* was expressed and authentically

"So Peter was kept in prison, but the church was earnestly praying to God for him. . . . When this [miraculous release from prison] had dawned on him, he went to the house of Mary the mother of John, also called Mark, where many people had gathered and were praying . . . . But Peter kept on knocking, and when they opened the door and saw him, they were astonished."
Acts 12:5,12, 16

experienced *in* us, *among* us, and *through us* to a watching, hurting, searching world. The closer and more transparent our love-relationship with God, the more intimate and real is our love-relationship with His people. This is why our prayer meetings were so meaningful. They grew out of the intimacy of our fellowship with God!

Questions: (Circle all that apply.)
• How would you describe the fellowship you have with God?

joyful	awkward	uninspiring
rewarding	exciting	uneventful
inspiring	powerful	nonexistent

• How would you describe your fellowship with other believers?

warm	joyful	tense
awkward	encouraging	exciting
healing	growing	stagnant

2. Fellowship in worship.
In addition to prayer, *koinonia* is also expressed through corporate worship. Take your Bible and read carefully the unusual "worship service" held by Paul and Silas in Acts 16:22-26.

Questions: (Answer based on what you read in the Bible.)
• What hardships did Paul and Silas undergo in this passage?

_____

• What did Paul and Silas do after being jailed?

_____

• What was the result? _____

Paul and Silas had been falsely accused, publicly humiliated, brutally beaten, and illegally imprisoned under maximum security. In spite of all this, they worshipped and praised God! This certainly got the attention of those around them. Then God released His awesome power. Many stories are told of Christians who, in difficult circumstances, gathered together and worshipped God. As they did, their love for God and each other grew to divine proportions and the power of God was released in their midst.

Our church often experienced *koinonia* during worship times as God granted us a powerful sense of His presence. Together we learned the meaning of Proverbs 9:10 which says: *"The fear of the Lord is the beginning of wisdom, and knowledge of the Holy One is understanding."* Week after week, in the presence of holy God, students would "process" the will of God in their lives. Some would respond to God's call to enter medicine, or engineering, or Christian ministry and missions. Couples would dedicate their relationship to God before the entire church. The Holy Spirit would take God's Word and teach and convince people of sin, righteousness, and judgment (John 16:8-9).

> As Christians experience the incredible, sacrificial love of God, they naturally want to respond in love.
>
> 100
> 50
> 0

The Holy Spirit guides people to a common goal and purpose, in order to accomplish His desires.

A Heart Yielded in Worship

One Sunday as we ended our morning service a university student came to the front of the church and said with great emotion: "God has been calling me into full-time Christian ministry but I have been running from His call. Today I've stopped running. I want my church to know I am surrendering my life to God's will, wherever He leads!" His testimony impacted several other young people in the church. Because of the intimate fellowship of the church body, the anguish of this student over his own disobedience convicted others that they, too, had been slow to respond to God's call. These also stood and shared the commitments they were making to the Lord that morning. The whole church family was encouraged, for we had been praying for the "Lord of the Harvest" to "thrust forth laborers" (Matthew 9:38) and we saw God answer our prayers that day. We stood in awe as we realized that Almighty God had intervened in our little church that morning.

3. Fellowship in gathering together.

Jesus said: *"Again, I tell you that if two of you on earth agree about anything you ask for, it will be done for you by my Father in heaven. For where two or three come together in my name, there am I with them" (Matthew 18:19-20).*

Questions:
• What are the criteria for God answering your prayers? _____

• Where does God promise to be present? _____

In this often-quoted passage, Jesus extended two promises. First, He said that when two or more Christians seek the mind of God together in prayer, He will grant their requests. The reason is not that God automatically grants the requests of groups of Christians. It is because the Holy Spirit guides people to a common goal and purpose, in order to accomplish *His* desires. Second, although God is *always* present with His children, Jesus said there is a dimension to His presence which can be felt only when Christians gather together and are of one heart and purpose. *Koinonia* can be experienced in any situation or circumstance where two or more Christians gather and are united by the Holy Spirit.

I have seen college students discover this *koinonia* in numerous ways. Some gathered in a fellow student's hospital room shortly before she was to have surgery. As they prayed for and encouraged her, a joy was evident that caused even non-Christian nurses to sense God's presence in the room. Greg was moments away from taking a three-hour oral exam when he was suddenly surrounded by friends from his church. They held an impromptu prayer meeting in the conference room that would soon be the scene of the most important exam of his life. I knew three students who met in a restaurant in order to minister to each other. In the midst of their conversation, a non-Christian from the next booth approached them and awkwardly asked if she might "join in." She had been listening and wanted to participate in the loving counsel that she had overheard. The prayer room in our church became a frequent gathering place for college students as two or three would pray for each other in times of difficulty. Groups of students would gather after the church services or prayer meetings and enjoy such a wonderful time of fellowship that they were reluctant to go home.

There is nothing in this life like the *koinonia* that comes from fellowship with God and fellow believers. It truly is a "taste of heaven" on earth!

Questions:

• Do you regularly experience the *koinonia* discussed in this lesson? ❏ Yes or ❏ No

• Have you joined a church where you can experience this *koinonia*? Describe what it is like. Are you encouraging fellow students to participate in this fellowship?

_____

• Have you isolated yourself from meaningful fellowship with other believers? If so, why?

_____

• Do you trust the people of God? Do you make your life open to fellow Christians?

_____

• What did God say to you during your study today?

_____

• What will you do as a result?

_____

LESSON 5
Together in Missions

In 1727, a church of 300 people gathered in Herrnhut, Saxony. There had been little spiritual power evident in this church's early days. However, the young pastor, Nicolas Zinzendorf, called on the people to pray. On August 27, 24 men and 24 women committed to pray around the clock. This unbroken prayer time lasted for over 100 years! Six months after their prayers began, the Holy Spirit was working so powerfully among them that the pastor asked if any were willing to release their lives to God in missions to the West Indies, Greenland, Turkey, and Lapland. The next day 26 people stepped forward, committing their lives to spreading the Gospel around the world. By 1792 that church of 300 had sent 300 missionaries around the world. They ministered to groups of people never previously reached by the gospel. One Moravian (as they were called) missionary, had a life-changing influence on John and Charles Wesley which led to their conversions. They in turn were influential in the Great Awakening that spread across England and North America during the 1700s. Many years later, when the modern mission movement began, missionaries would arrive at remote parts of the globe and discover that a missionary from that small church had already been there. One small church chose to go on mission with God and He used them to impact the world.[2]

"We are therefore Christ's ambassadors, as though God were making his appeal through us. We implore you on Christ's behalf: Be reconciled to God."
2 Corinthians 5:20

"As God's fellow workers we urge you not to receive God's grace in vain. For he says, 'In the time of my favor I heard you, and in the day of salvation I helped you.' I tell you, now is the time of God's favor, now is the day of salvation."
2 Corinthians 6:1-2

God's invitation to you is to join *His* work to redeem people and to impact a world through *your* church. *Notice what Paul said about the churches of his day in the Scripture to the left.*

Questions:
• Look at the Scripture in the sidebar; what did Paul say every Christian was supposed to do? _____

• According to 2 Corinthians 6:1, who are you working with? _____

In Scripture, we see that the heart and purpose of God is for the *corporate* people of God to be on mission with Him. The Great Commission and the promise of the Holy Spirit was given to the people of God, together in the church(es).

Under Christ's Direction
Take your Bible and read Ephesians 1:17-23 and in the space at the left, list the things Paul prayed for the church(es).

Questions:
• What did God do according to verse 22? Who did He do this for?

_____

• How is the church described in verse 23?

_____

Paul prayed not only that they would come to know God better, but that they would realize the glorious inheritance that was theirs as members of the "saints." He prayed that they would realize the "incomparably great power" that had been placed in Christ. Christ now rules the entire universe. God has placed everything under Christ's control and has done this *for* the church *which is His body.* The risen, triumphant Lord has been given to the church as its Head. Christ directs the church to fulfill God's plans to redeem mankind. Christ Himself directs His church. What more exciting group could you be a part of than this?

Our Mission
While I served as a pastor in Canada we faced a big challenge. Canada was largely apathetic to the gospel and only a small minority of its people were born-again Christians. Our church was small and had limited resources. Yet Christ, the Head of our church, led us to seek to evangelize our nation for Him. He directed us to cities, towns, and villages where there was no gospel witness and provided the resources to begin churches, build buildings, and send preachers and Bible teachers to those who needed to hear the good news of Christ.

Our students were part of a church that was on mission with God to redeem an entire nation and the world. When we began a new mission church, God would call out some to be involved in that work. Students would agree to go each Sunday to teach

Sunday School at the mission. Others would go to play the piano or make outreach visits. Some would work with youth while others would occasionally preach.

At times the efforts of students could be quite humorous. One nervous student drove two hours to preach at a mission. At the front of the little auditorium was a makeshift pulpit, consisting of a table topped with a portable lectern to hold the preacher's notes. In front of the lectern was a beautiful flower arrangement. As our preacher-in-training nervously gripped the lectern, he was oblivious to the fact that it was nudging the flower arrangement closer and closer to the edge of the table. At a climactic moment in his sermon, he sent the flowers crashing to the floor! Aghast, he raced around the table and frantically tried to reassemble the flower arrangement as the congregation struggled to suppress their laughter! This student went on to become a pastor and continues to serve the Lord faithfully.

Another student volunteered to live in a native Indian community in order to minister to the people there. In his attempt to control the acres of grassland surrounding the humble parsonage, he set the field on fire. Whipped by wind and unhindered by water, (since the young pastor had neglected to secure hoses), the fire threatened to engulf the entire community! Today, he is in full-time Christian ministry.

One of our mission churches invited a student to preach one Sunday. As he drove over unmarked country roads, he unknowingly took a wrong turn! Approaching the town just in time for the service, he noticed a sign welcoming him to Lanigan. He was supposed to be preaching in *Leroy*! Panicking, he turned around and raced across the gravel roads, screeching into Leroy at 11:30. A fellow student, there to direct the music, was leading the congregation in prayer, planning to pray as long as he had to until the preacher arrived! As the flustered preacher burst into the sanctuary, he was met with a not-too-spiritual glare by the music director! Nevertheless, God blessed their efforts; they are both in full-time ministry today!

I could tell you story after amusing story of the ministry efforts of our university students and how God used them in spite of themselves! It was never their ability that mattered as much as their availability. They recognized that Christ was their Head and whatever He assigned them to do He would also enable them to accomplish. He could overcome their limitations! Together the students in our church watched God build His kingdom across those Canadian prairies. **God's invitation to you is for you to link your life with His church and then to be on mission with Him.**

The Wisdom of God
Take your Bible and read Ephesians 3:8-12, 21.

Questions:
• What was Paul assigned to do in the Scripture you just read? (verses 8 and 9)

_____

• What vehicle does God use to display the many sides to His wisdom? (verse 10)

_____

• To whom did God display His wisdom? _____

> Christ now rules the entire universe. God has placed everything under Christ's control and has done this *for* the church *which is His body.*

100

50

0

• Where will God put His glory? (verse 21) _____

• In light of these verses, how important is it that you be involved in a church *as God planned it*? _____

Paul had received clear instructions from the Head of the church regarding his assignment, to proclaim to the Gentiles the "unending, boundless, fathomless, incalculable, exhaustless riches of Christ" (Amplified version). He was also to teach them that God's plan from the beginning was to reveal His infinite wisdom to all the angelic powers and principalities *through the church*. Does that mean the church is perfect? No! But it does mean that God has designed special things to occur in the church that will happen nowhere else. It is through the church's obedience and worship that God receives glory and demonstrates His wisdom to all the universe.

I was the pastor of a church in one of the highest crime areas of San Francisco. Our community was filled with drugs, violence, crime, and divorce. As a young pastor, I could not begin to provide answers for the plethora of need that surrounded our church. One night there was a domestic quarrel in our neighborhood in which the husband had barricaded himself in his home with a shotgun. The police turned to our church for help, and God used us to help bring about a peaceful end. One evening worship service was interrupted by 23 bikers from a gang called the "Untouchables," who brazenly sauntered into the back of the church and sat down. All 23 leaned back in their chairs, defying the church to affect them. But God had other plans! Within a year, all but one had given their hearts to Christ as their Savior. We saw young people addicted to drugs and alcohol released from their bondage. We witnessed marriages that were virtually over, restored through the ministry of Christ in our church. People suffering debilitating depression found joy for the first time in the fellowship of our church family. Those who had never before experienced unconditional love, found themselves surrounded by God's love through His people.

Questions:

• Do you believe God wants to use *your* church to impact your community? _____

• What must you adjust in your life in order to be a part of God's redemptive plan for your church? _____

• What did God say to you during your study today?

_____

• What will you do as a result?

_____

[1]"Persecution in the Early Church, *Christian History* Issue 27 (Vol. IX, No. 3), 33.
[2]Leslie K. Tarr, "A Prayer Meeting that Lasted 100 Years," *Christian History* (Volume 1, No. 1), 18.

№ 7 KINGDOM LIVING:
GETTING THE BIGGER PICTURE

0   10   20   40   •   100

INTRODUCTION
Kingdom Citizens

All over Daytona Beach and Panama City Beach, Florida, cold beer was consumed by the truck-load, and sun bathers gyrated to the tune "Let's Talk About Sex" blasting over loudspeakers. It was spring break; these students were going to "party till they dropped."

God invited a group of Christian college students to reach out to these who needed to know of God's love. They called their outreach effort "BeachReach." Almost 800 college students from 50 different campuses gave up their spring break and, many at their own expense, traveled to Florida to share Christ. They offered a free pancake breakfast every morning, van rides for those too drunk to drive, and a crisis intervention hotline for students who "reached the bottom." Many students gave their lives to Christ. Four runaways, as young as 13, accepted Christ as Lord and Savior and returned home. One student who became a Christian during the last van ride of the week said he had heard the gospel from six different Christians and concluded: "They seemed to be the only truly happy people here!" One group was pursuing hedonistic pleasures. The emptier they felt, the harder they partied. The other belonged to Christ; their pleasure came from honoring God and serving Him.

LESSON 1
The Kingdom's Qualities
Kingdom Pursuits

What is your greatest priority? Place a number from one to eight beside each with 1 being the most important:

___ going to heaven when you die ___ seeking the kingdom of God
___ graduating from university ___ being happy
___ getting married ___ pursuing a successful career
___ having children ___ fulfilling your dreams

Did you mark the kingdom of God as number one? If so, did you put it first because you knew it was the right answer? Most of us are familiar with this chapter's memory verse, but do we really know what it means? If you are to seek first the kingdom of God, it is important that you understand what this kingdom is like. *The kingdom of God is God's rule over all His creation.* He controls the universe and every person will ultimately give an account of their lives to Him. Every believer in every part of the world is a citizen of the kingdom. Every church where the Gospel is proclaimed belongs to the kingdom.

A Kingdom Invitation

In Matthew 13, Jesus gave a number of descriptions of what the kingdom of God means. As He did, He warned that not everyone would understand the "mysteries of the kingdom" (verse 11), but only those who were *citizens* of the kingdom. Jesus also recognized that people would respond differently to the invitation to the kingdom. Before studying the *qualities* of the kingdom, notice the various ways people *respond* to it in the Scripture in Matthew 13:3-8 located on the next page.

Questions:

• In the Scripture, circle the four results of sowing seed.

• Jesus said this parable illustrates four ways people respond to God's invitation. What four responses do you see? Circle them also.

When Jesus began His public ministry, He preached, *"Repent, for the kingdom of heaven is near" (Matthew 4:17).* Everywhere Jesus went He gave the same invitation: for people to become citizens of the kingdom of God. Some rejected His invitation and even went as far as crucifying Him. Others expressed interest, but were not willing to pay the price required. Others began to respond to the invitation of the gospel, but the cares and concerns of the world "choked out" their initial interest. However, there were those who willingly accepted the responsibilities of kingdom citizenship and God produced a great spiritual crop through their lives. The invitation to the kingdom of God is given to everyone. The difference is in our response.

Kingdom Qualities

Edward Kimball was a Sunday School teacher in a Congregationalist church in Boston where he taught a class for teenage boys. Convicted by the Holy Spirit that he did not know the spiritual condition of each of his students, he began to visit them individually to find out if they were Christians. Kimball visited the shoe store where one of his class members, an 18-year-old named Dwight, worked. In the room where he stocked shelves, Dwight Lyman Moody (1837-1899), gave his life to Christ. He went on to become an international evangelist, preaching to over 130,000 people in one day! He founded three schools and two publishing houses all of which are still in operation. It is estimated that in his lifetime, Moody traveled over one million miles and preached the gospel to one hundred million people.

One of those converted under Moody's ministry was John Wilbur Chapman (1859-1918); he too became a full-time evangelist. In addition, he wrote or edited 30 books and numerous pamphlets on the Christian life. William Ashley Sunday (1862-

1935), a professional baseball player, was converted as a result of Chapman's ministry and also became a full-time evangelist. It is estimated that 300,000 people gave their lives to Christ during his evangelistic meetings. One of the converts in Sunday's ministry was Mordecai Fowler Ham (1877-1961). Ham devoted his life to preaching the gospel and saw hundreds of thousands of conversions. During a revival meeting held in Charlotte, North Carolina, in 1934, William Frank Graham (1918-) was converted. Billy Graham was a shy sixteen-year old–an unlikely candidate for international ministry. However, as a teenager, he committed his life entirely into God's service and prayed that God might use him in His kingdom work. During Billy Graham's ministry, hundreds of millions of people have heard the gospel message and millions have responded in faith. On April 14, 1996 an estimated 2.5 *billion* people in 160 countries heard him present the gospel which was translated into 42 languages.

Did Edward Kimball know what would come of his obedience in 1855? Of course not. Did God? Certainly! Kimball was obedient to what God invited him to do and God used his obedience to bring millions into His kingdom. Every act of obedience carries with it the potential to mightily impact the kingdom of God. God invites *you* to obey His instructions for your life and to experience Him working in you to bring a world to Christ.

Notice what Jesus said the qualities of the kingdom would be like in Matthew 13.

1. The kingdom starts out small.
Take your Bible and read Matthew 13:31-32.

Questions:
• According to this parable, how does "kingdom work" start out?

_____

• How large does the work of the kingdom become?

_____

• Does "big" indicate success in God's kingdom? _____

You may be discouraged if your Christian student group is small or your church is not as large as others. Don't be. God chooses to work through the small and weak in order to demonstrate *His* power to a watching world. Furthermore, small beginnings do not necessarily mean a small finish. Most of God's greatest works have begun small, like the mustard seed.

2. The kingdom has a steady influence.
Read the verse to the right.

Question:
• How does yeast operate in a batch of dough? How would this apply to the work of God in society?

_____

> "A farmer went out to sow his seed. As he was scattering the seed, some fell along the path, and the birds came and ate it up. Some fell on rocky places, where it did not have much soil. It sprang up quickly, because the soil was shallow. But when the sun came up, the plants were scorched, and they withered because they had no root. Other seed fell among thorns, which grew up and choked the plants. Still other seed fell on good soil, where it produced a crop—a hundred, sixty or thirty times what was sown."
> **Matthew 13:3-8**

> "The kingdom of heaven is like yeast that a woman took and mixed into a large amount of flour until it worked all through the dough." **Matthew 13:33**

Yeast is not significant by itself. It's not flashy. It doesn't work in a loud, flamboyant way. But it gets the job done. One moment there is a small lump of dough, sitting inconspicuously in a bowl. Check a couple of hours later and the dough is bulging over the top and down the sides. God's kingdom works that way; He needs no marketing experts to help His kingdom have an impact! God works "behind the scenes," saving people one at a time. This happened in China. When the communists expelled all the Christian missionaries, many feared that Christianity would be extinguished in that country. Four decades later the Western world discovered, to their surprise, over one hundred million Christians! What happened? The kingdom of God had steadily grown, quietly spreading throughout the country. Your witness on campus will be similar. You may not always see instant or dramatic results to all that you do, but God will take your efforts and will work in people's lives you might not even be aware of.

3. It has great value.
Read the verses to the left.

Questions:
• In what two ways did Jesus describe the kingdom of God?

_____

_____

• How important was the kingdom of God to the people in the stories? How do you know?

_____

"The kingdom of heaven is like treasure hidden in a field. When a man found it, he hid it again, and then in his joy went and sold all he had and bought that field."
Matthew 13:44

"Again, the kingdom of heaven is like a merchant looking for fine pearls. When he found one of great value, he went away and sold everything he had and bought it."
Matthew 13:45-46

Jesus was teaching that becoming a citizen of the kingdom is the most important thing you will ever do. If becoming a Christian meant that you had to give up everything else, it would be worth it. We had university students join our church who paid a great price for their commitment to Christ. Their family members would ostracize them; parents would expel them from their house; friends would forsake them; relatives would boycott their weddings, and much more. I counseled many students who faced the painful truth that sometimes you must decide if the kingdom of God is more important than anything else. These students were convinced that it was, and God gave them the courage to stick to their decision.

4. It has eternal dimensions.
Take your Bible and read Matthew 13:47-50.

Questions:
• Who do the two kinds of fish represent in Jesus' parable?

_____   _____

• What are their two destinations?

_____   _____

When a fisherman draws in his nets, there are both good and bad fish (see also Matthew 13:24-30). For a time the fisherman allows the bad fish to remain with the good. But before he brings the fish home he discards the bad fish. Jesus was saying that the final judgment is not immediate, but it is definite. Kingdom citizens may even face persecution by non-citizens for a time. The wicked may prosper while the righteous suffer. Ultimately, however, God is absolutely just. You may be in a secular, ungodly university and feel surrounded by the forces of evil. Yet, Jesus assures His citizens that He has won the victory and that ultimately those who reject His invitation to the kingdom will be punished.

Questions:
• Do *you* find comfort in the fact that God will be absolutely just in His judgment of you? Why?

_____

• Check which of these four truths of the kingdom you are presently experiencing.
❑ The Kingdom starts out small.   ❑ It has great value.
❑ The Kingdom has a steady influence. ❑ It has eternal dimensions.

• How are you living your life as a kingdom citizen?

_____

The rules of God's kingdom are usually contradictory to the commonly held beliefs of modern society. In the exercise below, put a "K" beside those principles which belong to God's *kingdom*, and a "W" beside those things commonly taught by the "world."

1. ___ Size is the best indicator of success.
2. ___ Marketing is everything!
3. ___ What is important is obedience.
4. ___ Eat, drink and be merry!
5. ___ The key to success is a heart that is right toward God.
6. ___ Live for eternity, not time.

Prince or Pauper?
Samuel Clemens told the delightful tale of two boys who, by freak circumstances, had their roles reversed. One was a pauper, living in dire poverty, abused and suffering hardship. The other was a prince who lived in comfort and luxury. When they switched places, the prince was forced to live the life of a beggar, while the pauper was pampered and coddled. The frustrated prince was forced to live far below the means he knew were his.

Unfortunately, many Christians live like paupers when they are actually sons and daughters of the King. They live on meager spiritual resources and suffer constant defeat. In reality they are children of the King and therefore have access to all of His resources. God has given *His* children everything they need. It would be a tragedy to live with anything less (see Romans 8:14-17; 2 Corinthians 1:20; Ephesians 1:3, 2:4-7).

> Jesus taught that becoming a citizen of the kingdom is the most important thing you will ever do. If becoming a Christian meant that you had to give up everything else, it would be worth it.
>
> 100 — 50 — 0

Questions:

• Are you presently living like a child of the King? What evidence is there of this?

_____

• What did God say to you during your study today?

_____

_____

• What will you do as a result?

_____

_____

LESSON 2
The Kingdom's Keys

Last year I had one of the most embarrassing and frustrating experiences of my life when I flew to Richmond, Virginia, to speak at a conference. There was a terrible snowstorm and I was eager to arrive at the conference center. I rented a new car with every modern, convenient device available. I felt certain that if any vehicle could maneuver through the storm that day it would be this one. Nevertheless the car became stuck in a snowdrift. Having lived many years on the Canadian prairies, I felt somewhat like an "expert" in freeing snowbound cars! From experience I knew my strategy would differ depending on whether the car was front- or rear-wheel drive. I wasn't sure which type of car this was, so not knowing any other way to tell which tires were spinning in the snow, I left the car in "drive," and got out to take a look. The wind was howling around me and the snow was blinding. Peering at the wheels I determined which tires were spinning uselessly in an icy rut. Shivering in the cold, I hurried to get back in the car. Just then, a strong wind seized the car door and slammed it shut. As soon as the door closed, the doors automatically locked! Frustrated and helpless, I stood outside in the blizzard watching the car, running and in gear, spin deeper in the drift. The car heater continued to fill the car with warm air. The windshield wipers kept the windshield free from snow. The driver's seat was tilted comfortably; the radio played relaxing music. There I stood, shivering *outside* in the snow, *without* the keys! All the comforts and conveniences of the vehicle were absolutely worthless to me as without the keys I had no access to them.

Sadly I know Christians who struggle through life without ever realizing they *do* have access to God and all His resources for a victorious and abundant life. Jesus repeatedly said: "Don't worry!" Why? Because He knew the King. He knew His Father's love, mercy, grace, faithfulness, forgiveness, and kindness and He knew that it was senseless to worry when God had made such bountiful provision for citizens of His kingdom. Yet we still worry about exams, health, assignments, finances, friendships, the future, job security, parents, and a thousand other things! Our concerns may be real, but we can miss the important truth that God stands ready to meet the needs of His children.

Keys of the Kingdom

"I will give you the keys of the kingdom of heaven; whatever you bind on earth will be bound in heaven, and whatever you loose on earth will be loosed in heaven." (Matthew 16:19).

Questions:

• What do you think Jesus meant by "keys of the kingdom"?

_____

• What are you to do with them? How do you do this?

_____

_____

Suppose a wealthy man adopted an impoverished orphan as his son. Imagine that the benevolent man took the boy to his mansion and showed him through every luxurious room. In each room were different treasures. At the end of the tour, the man handed his new son a set of keys and said, "These keys will open any door in this house. If there is anything you or your friends ever need, help yourself!" In Matthew 16:19, Jesus was telling His disciples that because of their special relationship with the Father, they were being given a set of keys. As children of God, they now had direct access to God and to His heavenly storerooms. Because of their relationship with *Him*, they had access to Him and therefore to His resources.

God's Promises to Kingdom Citizens

Read carefully the wonderful promises made to kingdom citizens in the Scripture to the right.

State these verses in terms of *your* life as a student:

2 Corinthians 9:8: _____

_____

Philippians 4:13: _____

_____

Philippians 4:19: _____

_____

These are encouraging promises. They are *invitations* extended to Christians. God wants us to seek Him and His provisions. Remember what it *cost* God in order to provide these resources. It cost Him His Son. Will you accept His invitation to rely on Him for all your needs?

"And God is able to make all grace abound to you, so that in all things at all times, having all that you need, you will abound in every good work." **2 Corinthians 9:8**

"I can do everything through him who gives me strength." **Philippians 4:13**

"And my God will meet all your needs according to his glorious riches in Christ Jesus." **Philippians 4:19**

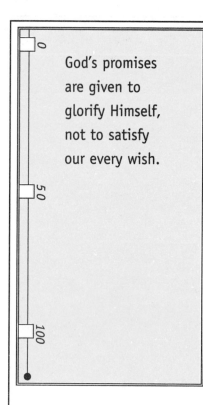

God's promises are given to glorify Himself, not to satisfy our every wish.

A word of caution here. God's promises are given to glorify Himself, not to satisfy our every wish. Don't be like the preschooler who was frustrated because his parents would not allow him to do what he asked. In frustrated defiance he shouted, "I can do EVERYTHING through Him who gives me strength. Philippians 4:13!" This little boy's Scripture memory was commendable; his theology was a bit off!

Scripture holds a great number of promises for God's children. List additional promises of God that have been particularly meaningful to you. Give scriptural references if possible:

Promise 1: _____
Promise 2: _____
Promise 3: _____
Promise 4: _____
Promise 5: _____

Keys Open Doors

On a Sunday morning in October, 1995, a five-year-old boy and his three-year-old sister from Brossard, Quebec, couldn't wait for their parents to wake up and feed them breakfast. So, snatching the keys to the family van, they drove almost a mile to McDonalds! The little boy had to virtually lie down in order to reach the gas pedal, occasionally popping up to see where he was going! A cashier at the gas station next door to McDonalds was taken aback when she saw a "driverless" van approach. Then, to her amazement, the door opened and two small children in pajamas and bare feet climbed out. The young boy later told police, "I had my seat belt on, and so did my sister. I'm *not* going to go to prison."[1]

Those two children discovered that the keys gave them access to something much bigger and more powerful than themselves. So it is for the Christian. By ourselves we are weak but we hold the keys to God's bountiful kingdom. It may be that you grew up in a home where you were not affirmed and love was not expressed. Even as a Christian you may long to experience love. It would be tragic for you to go through life longing to be loved when you hold the keys to God's promises such as Romans 8:35-38, which says that *nothing* can *ever* separate you from God's love. Or, perhaps you are a Christian who has fallen into sin. You may feel terrible about your failure and fear that God would never relate to someone so prone to sin. It would be futile for you to live a defeated life when 1 John 1:9 promises that if you confess your sins, God is faithful to forgive you and to cleanse you, making you pure in His sight. Promises like these and many others are yours if you will accept them as God's invitation to you.

When Jesus gave the keys of the kingdom to His disciples, they came with a responsibility. That is, the disciples' special relationship with the heavenly Father and their access to His resources was not to be hoarded for themselves. Just as *they* knew God, the disciples could invite *others* to establish this same relationship with Him. Thus God's provisions would be accessible to them also. For example, you might have a friend who is depressed and discouraged. You may not have wise words to share or power to change his circumstances. Yet, you will have the "keys of the kingdom." You will have access to Philippians 4:6-7, which promises that if we take our cares to God, *His* peace, which surpasses comprehension, will surround our hearts and minds until we are no longer anxious even in the midst of the most difficult circumstances. It is not *your* answers people need, nor *your* peace, nor *your* resources. People need God and what only He can give. Yet *you* have been given the keys to God's storehouse and can guide people to God in order that they can receive His provision for their problems.

Questions:

• Take a moment and think of three people you know who are experiencing need. *List those people in the space to the right and then indicate their specific need.*

• *Now look back over the list and write a Scripture which addresses each need you have listed.*

Commit yourself to:

First, tell your friend of the Scriptural promise God has given that can be theirs if they will accept it in faith;

Second, begin praying that this Scripture will become real and personal to your friend. When you look at the magnificent ways people like the Apostle Paul prayed for others in Ephesians 1:15-23; 3:14-21; and Colossians 1:9-12, it is hard to pray anything more uplifting for people than *this*. You have the "keys" to these promises. Commit to pray them for others and watch to see how God implements these promises into their lives.

• What did God say to you during your study today?

_____

• What will you do as a result?

_____

LESSON 3
The Kingdom's Implications

It's amazing how far some people will go to gain notoriety! They devote their entire lives to pursuing fame. For example, one man placed two cables in his mouth and held two Cessna aircraft, engines running at 2,400 rpm's with a combined horsepower of 310, for three seconds. Why? To claim a world record of course! Another man collected 2,561 different brands of chewing-gum to set a record. Did you know that the longest single apple peel is 52.51 meters? And were you aware that the fastest noodle maker can make 4,096 noodles in 58.2 seconds? The world's greatest yo-yoer can do 21,633 yo-yo tricks in three hours. When interviewed, this man said, not surprisingly, "yo-yo is my life." Sadly, some people devote their lives to trivial, eternally inconsequential pursuits.

There are many purposes to which one could devote one's life. Some are more noble than others. In each case, a person must decide just how serious they will be about their commitment.

When Jesus stood on the seashore and invited John to follow Him, John had no idea what this would involve. John released his life to Jesus, not knowing what it would cost, where he might have to travel, or what might be asked of him. He had come face to face with God's Son and he knew it was an invitation he must accept. As a result, John experienced life with dimensions beyond his wildest dreams. He walked with the Son of God. He witnessed Jesus performing miracles. He saw God raise people from the dead. He wrote several books of holy Scripture. He cared for the mother of the Son of God. His life influenced millions of people over the ensuing centuries. **John accepted God's invitation to live as a child of God in the kingdom of the Son of God (Colossians 1:13).**

Jesus invited His followers to consider the implications of belonging to God's kingdom:

1. Kingdom before family.
Read the Scripture to the left.

Questions:
• How did Jesus say your relationships with others should compare to your relationship with Him?

_____

• What does this mean you should do if you ever face a choice between pleasing your family and pleasing Jesus?

_____

• Have you ever had to choose between the wishes of your parents or family members and obeying God? Write an example in the space to the left.

Perhaps the most difficult invitations you will ever receive from God are those which require you to do things to which your parents object. I have seen many students weep as they agonized over the alienation they were experiencing from their parents because they had been baptized, or had committed their life to missions, or had witnessed to their siblings. We once had two university students arrive at our home on Christmas day. They had been told to leave their parents' home because they had been talking about the Lord. In the years that followed they sought to honor their parents, treating them with respect, while remaining obedient to God's direction.

2. Kingdom after counting the cost.
"Suppose one of you wants to build a tower. Will he not first sit down and estimate the cost to see if he has enough money to complete it? For if he lays the foundation and is not able to finish it, everyone who sees it will ridicule him, saying, 'This fellow began to build and was not able to finish'" (Luke 14:28-30). Read the verses on the next page.

"If anyone comes to me and does not hate his father and mother, his wife and children, his brothers and sisters—yes, even his own life—he cannot be my disciple. And anyone who does not carry his cross and follow me cannot be my disciple."
Luke 14:26-27

Questions:
• What is the truth found in both the passages on the previous page and to the right?

_____

• Why is it important to count the cost before following Jesus?

_____

Jesus cautioned: "You must count the cost if you are to follow Me." Make no mistake, following Jesus will cost you! If you try to live the Christian life unaware that Jesus expects absolute obedience to *everything* He tells you to do, you may reach a point in your Christian faith where you are unwilling go further. If you "count the cost" of your commitment to Christ, then God's work in you will not be incomplete or abandoned when the going gets tough. Remember, the cost of *not* following Jesus is *always* far greater!

He Should Have Counted the Cost!

A student in my church, Rick, wanted to impress a girl on a date. He took her to one of the nicest restaurants in the city and offered to treat her to anything on the menu. Unfortunately, he had not accurately "counted the cost." His date ordered a steak dinner, with *all* the trimmings! *and dessert!!* When the bill came, Rick panicked. He was $10 short. Suddenly, he remembered that the ash tray in his jalopy held his parking meter money. Coolly, he excused himself and sauntered to the door where he fairly flew outside to his car. Removing the full ash tray, he stuffed it under his jacket and returned to the restaurant. The red-faced Casanova then confessed his quandary to his understanding companion. Laughing, she took the ash tray to the drug store next door, and had the mound of change converted into dollar bills. There was just enough! The chagrined student paid the bill and meekly left the restaurant, determined that *next* time, he would count the cost (or carry a credit card!).

Sadly, I have seen Christians who did not "count the cost" before embarking on their Christian pilgrimage. Their motive for accepting Christ was to ensure a place in heaven when they died. They wanted to be "eligible" for a wide assortment of blessings, but wanted only minimal obligations. Then God began to exercise His Lordship over their lives. Suddenly there was a cost involved. Perhaps it was their prejudicial attitudes He wanted to change. Or maybe God asked them to leave their large, comfortable church to join a mission work in the downtown core. God might have asked them to take a job overseas where they could be a support to the missionaries in that country. They realized that there was much more required of them than they had bargained for. Rather than being transformed into an effective servant of God, they became spiritually stagnant and of no use to God. How much easier it would have been for them if they'd entered God's kingdom prepared to pay the price.

Question:
• Do you think you clearly understand what God expects of you as a Christian and are you prepared to make the kind of commitment His lordship requires? Explain.

_____

"Or suppose a king is about to go to war against another king. Will he not first sit down and consider whether he is able with ten thousand men to oppose the one coming against him with twenty thousand? If he is not able, he will send a delegation while the other is still a long way off and will ask for terms of peace."
Luke 14:31-32

Jesus said that if your response to God's invitation comes into conflict with your commitment to material possessions and ambitions, there should be no question what you should do.

3. The kingdom before possessions.
Take your Bible and read Luke 14:33.

Write the truth of this verse in terms of your life and obedience to God in the space to the left.

Jesus said that if your response to God's invitation comes into conflict with your commitment to material possessions and ambitions, there should be no question what you should do. He was saying that your possessions should have no hold upon your life. You ought to be able to part with *everything* God asks of you. If you possess anything that hinders you from being on mission with God, get rid of it! One fine student couple heard about mission work in a foreign country and became concerned about the needs of the missionaries. This couple had limited financial resources, but they believed God was inviting them to get involved with Him in this work. They canceled their cable TV service and sent this money to the mission field.

Questions:
• Do you have possessions or financial commitments that prevent you from doing all God wants you to do? Pray and ask God to reveal anything that hinders you from doing His will. *Write down what He tells you and then release those things to God.*

• As you search your heart, would you be willing to go *anywhere* God might ask you to go? If not, where are you unwilling to go?

_____

• What do you sense God wants to do in and through your life right now? Are you willing for Him to do this work in you?

_____

• What did God say to you during your study today?

_____

• What will you do as a result?

_____

LESSON 4
The Kingdom's Power
Scared to Death
As a college student, Dennis responded to God's invitation to serve in summer missions in the Philippines. One of the activities Dennis enjoyed was playing basketball with the young people. Dennis was an African-American, 5' 8" tall. Many of the Filipinos had never seen an American, and fewer had seen an African-American. As he played basketball, Filipinos would gather around the court to watch, thinking he was

actually a professional basketball player. One day, an elderly man approached Dennis and asked him to go with him to tell his village about Jesus. Dennis readily agreed. Once he had committed to go, he was startled to hear that the last missionary who had gone to this village had been killed by communist guerrillas. After some hesitation Dennis went, albeit fearfully. The first people he shared Jesus with accepted Christ as their Lord and Savior. Dennis was jubilant, but as he left their house he came face to face with a gang of communist guerrillas holding machine guns. Praying for God's strength, he carefully approached the men. Their leader stepped forward and asked, "Are you a missionary?"

"Yes," he replied.

"Did you tell about Jesus in that house?"

"Yes."

Then the soldier smiled, "We read about you. You come out of retirement. You score 50 points against the Knicks." Then he turned to his fellow soldiers and exclaimed, "It's Michael Jordan!" Dennis was relieved and amused that he could have been mistaken for one of the most famous basketball players in the world! As he returned to the United States, he carried with him the thrill of having experienced God's protection and knowing that God had used him to impact a village on the other side of the world.

Jesus wants you to be a "world Christian." *Notice His invitation in the verse to the right.*

Questions:
• What did Jesus promise His followers?

_____

• What did He instruct His followers to do? _____

Jesus gave this incredible invitation to His timid disciples to touch and change their world. He said they would receive "power." This is the Greek word from which we get the word "dynamite." Jesus said their power would not be inherent to themselves, but would come from the presence of the Holy Spirit in their lives. The Holy Spirit's role was to guide, equip, and empower the people of God to be instruments for God's redemptive purposes. They would begin in *Jerusalem*, the center of Jewish religion. They would go to *Judea*, the rural and less-traveled areas of the nation. They would go still farther afield into *Samaria*. This was an area not too distant in miles but culturally on the other side of the world. The Spirit would have to remove the disciples' prejudices and fears in order for them to reach the people in Samaria. Finally, the Spirit would take them to the *"ends of the earth."* They had a narrow view of their world. All the nations but theirs were considered "unclean." Yet Jesus was saying that God wanted to evangelize the world through *them*.

Questions:
• Are you presently experiencing the presence and power of the Holy Spirit guiding you? _____

> "You will receive power when the Holy Spirit comes on you; and you will be my witnesses in Jerusalem, and in all Judea and Samaria, and to the ends of the earth." **Acts 1:8**

• How is the Spirit guiding you to share God's full provision for life with others?

_____

_____

Serving God in Mexico

Twenty-five college students from Louisiana sensed God inviting them to minister at a Christian encampment in Acuna, Mexico. Raising the necessary funds and working out all the details of the trip had been a challenge, yet God had provided for all their needs. At the end of each day, they gathered to worship. One evening as Mario, a laborer, was hurrying home from a long day's work, he cut through the encampment to save time. As he walked alone in the darkness, he heard singing coming from a house nearby. Curious, he climbed on top of a wall for a better view. One of the students noticed Mario and invited him to join them. That night Mario became a child of God. Those students who had sacrificially traveled from Louisiana to Mexico came to understand that God's kingdom extended far beyond their campus.

Questions:
• Had Mario been the *only* convert that week, do you think the students' sacrifice would have been worthwhile? _____

• Do you have the world in your heart? One of the best-known Scripture verses says: *"For God so loved the world that He gave His one and only Son . . ." (John 3:16).* Do you love the *world* the way God does? God loved it so much, He gave the One He loved the most, His Son, to redeem it. Take the following test to see how much of the "world" is in your heart:

I keep informed of world events. ❏ never ❏ sometimes ❏ regularly	I give money to foreign mission causes. ❏ never ❏ sometimes ❏ regularly
I pray for the people in other countries. ❏ never ❏ sometimes ❏ regularly	I attend missions meetings. ❏ never ❏ sometimes ❏ regularly
I pray specifically for world crises. ❏ never ❏ sometimes ❏ regularly	I study about foreign countries. ❏ never ❏ sometimes ❏ regularly
I pray for missionaries around the world. ❏ never ❏ sometimes ❏ regularly	I befriend international students. ❏ never ❏ sometimes ❏ regularly
I read mission magazines and books. ❏ never ❏ sometimes ❏ regularly	other_____ ❏ never ❏ sometimes ❏ regularly
I have served in short-term missions. ❏ never ❏ sometimes ❏ regularly	

• How did you do? Would you like to check more "regularly"? What could you do to increase your involvement in world missions?

_____

_____

I am always disappointed when I find Christians who are completely unconcerned with what is happening in the world. They don't watch the international news or read about world events. They know little about missions. They do not know the heart of God for the people of the world. They do not give to support missions nor do they pray for missionaries. Yet Jesus clearly *commanded* us to be "world Christians."

Question:
• Would you call yourself a "world Christian?" Do others see you as a world Christian?

_____

_____

Bricklaying for God

In the summer of 1995, the Canadian Southern Baptist Seminary in Cochrane, Alberta appealed for help to construct a new classroom building. The school had no resources, and they prayed that God would provide laborers for this project. A small church in Texas heard their request. In their church was a bricklayer. His father and son, both bricklayers also, were members of the church as well. When they heard that the seminary needed to lay 50,000 bricks, they volunteered to go. Then the pastor agreed to go and run the forklift. Teenagers said they were willing to mix the mortar. Senior adults offered to build and load scaffolding. Women volunteered to cook the meals. They formed a work team of 20 and headed to Canada. Their work day began at 5:30 a.m. with their first break at 7 a.m. for breakfast. The crew did a magnificent job, providing a strong Christian witness to the entire community. As word spread of their sacrificial efforts, requests began to come from all over the world where bricklayers were needed to construct buildings for Christian causes. Now that little church has more offers than they know what to do with! One church, willing and prepared to respond to God's invitation, is impacting their world for Christ.

Questions:
• What is God building into your life that He might use to impact your world?

_____

• How is the world being changed because of you?

_____

• What did God say to you during your study today?

_____

_____

> Jesus gave an incredible invitation to His timid disciples to touch and change their world. He said they would receive "power" not inherent to themselves, but from the presence of the Holy Spirit in their lives.

• What will you do as a result?

_____

_____

LESSON 5
The Kingdom's Accounting

Recently a man approached me at the close of a conference. He shared how as a young boy he had sensed God leading him to become a doctor in order to serve on the mission field. He had entered medicine, specializing in the immune system. After graduation he accepted a position in research at a major university. He married and was active in his church. However, he realized that God's invitation given so many years earlier, still stood. Now he had to decide how to respond. He realized he would have to give an account for how he responded to God's invitation. A year later I rejoiced to hear that he had been appointed to Uganda as a medical missionary! He had accepted God's invitation and was now touching a world with his critical knowledge and skill in AIDS research.

The Apostle Paul was daily motivated by a keen awareness that his life, at all times, must please God. *Read what he wrote in the verses at the left.*

Questions:
• What was a major motivating factor affecting Paul's life?

_____

• What does it mean to be "accountable" to God?

_____

Paul was one of the greatest saints of all time. He shared life-transforming messages, started churches, wrote letters which became Scripture, and developed the church's theology. Scripture reveals that the motivating principle behind all he did was the knowledge of Christ's love and that *every* person would have to give an account of his actions before a holy and absolutely just God. We tend to think judgment is reserved for nonbelievers. Yet, Paul said he knew the "fear" of the Lord. Paul had a reverent concern that he would never have to stand ashamed before his Savior.

Questions:
• How do you feel about one day standing before God and giving an account of your actions, both good and bad?

_____

_____

• Do you have a reverent "fear" of God? What is the evidence of this?

_____

"So we make it our goal to please him, whether we are at home in the body or away from it. For we must all appear before the judgment seat of Christ, that each one may receive what is due him for the things done while in the body, whether good or bad." **2 Corinthians 5:9-10**

Notice in the Scripture to the right how Paul said you could evaluate the things you do in this life.

Questions:
• What will happen to the things you invest in during your life?

_____

• Is it possible to do nothing of eternal value and still enter heaven? How?

_____

• What kind of works will last in heaven? _____

Paul wanted no disappointments at the end of his life so he left nothing to chance. He knew full well that it was possible to live as a Christian and have nothing to show for it when it was over. Paul used the vivid imagery of fire cleansing and burning away impurities. Paul said God's judgment would be like a fire that burned away every sinful act. When every sin is removed, whatever is left will be acceptable to God.

Questions:
• What activities are you presently involved in that would survive God's cleansing fires? *List them in the space to the right.*

• Do you have thoughts, attitudes, habits, or sins that you know would not meet God's standards in judgment? How could you deal with them now?

_____

• How are you investing your life wisely? _____

An Expanded Vision

John was a successful college minister who worked faithfully on his campus. He began to feel an intensifying burden to establish new campus ministries on the major universities around the world. He traveled with his students to a foreign university and found that students there were responsive to the gospel message. He felt impressed to take students from his campus and visit the major universities across the former Soviet Union. To his surprise, the people were not only receptive to the gospel message but urged him to return. John eventually felt God leading him to resign his campus job and to devote himself full-time to working on universities around the world.

Conclusion

Today there are thousands of college students who are responding to God's invitation to be on mission with Him. This may be the generation that sees more university students involved in missions across North America and the world than any other time in history. Students responding to God's invitation are taking the Gospel to the inner cities of America, to prisons, to hospitals for the dying, to the political offices of Washington, DC, and other world capitals, to professional sports teams, and to the military. Christian students are realizing that God has far more for them than they could have imagined as they impact the world like never before.

"His work will be shown for what it is, because the Day will bring it to light. It will be revealed with fire, and the fire will test the quality of each man's work. If what he has built survives, he will receive his reward. If it is burned up, he will suffer loss; he himself will be saved, but only as one escaping through the flames."
1 Corinthians 3:13-15

Questions:

• During this course, you have been challenged to respond to God's invitation. Look back over the course and write in the space to the left everything you committed to God during your study.

• Take a moment to pray about each one.

• Who have you asked to hold you accountable to the commitments you have made? List their names.

_____   _____

_____   _____

• As you come to the end of this study, what is the one thing above all others you know you MUST do as a result of what God is saying to you?

_____

• Do you need to make any of your decisions public in your church or Christian organization? If so, when will you do this?

_____

• Are you keeping a record of all that God has invited you to do, and your corresponding obedience? If not, begin making a list of: 1) what God invited you to do; 2) the date He spoke to you; 3) your response.

We pray that you will take seriously God's invitation to you. We have both experienced God's invitation and realize the incredible joy of being used to influence the world for Christ. We sincerely want you to have this experience too. **How will YOU respond to God's invitation? God's invitation is your greatest challenge!**

_____
"Tot takes sister for breakfast in family van," *Calgary Herald*, October 12, 1995.

You have completed the beginning! Are there areas you have studied which you need to understand more fully? Go back and review that material again. The rest of your life depends on your understanding this information. You have the tools. Keep them for the rest of your life.

0   10   20   40   100